PENGUIN BOOKS

THIN-THINK

Jane Walmsley is a television producer, presenter and writer. She was born in Pittsburgh, Pennsylvania, but has been based in London since the early seventies. She is married to Nigel Walmsley, Chief Executive of Carlton Television. They have a teenage daughter, Katie.

Jane has presented several major television current affairs series for the BBC and ITV. In 1986 she formed her own independent television production company, Jane Walmsley Productions. She was soon commissioned by Channel 4 to produce *Hot House People*, a documentary series on efforts to enhance intelligence in children. It has since been seen in thirty-five countries.

Jane began her career as presenter of the evening 'drive time' news show for Capital Radio in 1973. She eventually became the station's head of documentaries, collecting several industry awards for journalism before joining BBC television in 1980. There, she co-presented the weekly network series *Out of Court*, and eventually moved to ITV to co-present the flagship documentary series *First Tuesday*. More recent productions include *Mother's Day* for Channel 4 (1990), and *The Cheque is in the Post* and *Many Happy Returns?* for BBC Television (1992 and 1993). At present, she is working on a variety of factual and entertainment projects.

Jane Walmsley is the author of two other books, *Hot House People* (1987) and *Brit-Think, Ameri-Think: A Transatlantic Survival Guide* (1986).

THIN-THINK

Jane Walmsley

PENGUIN BOOKS

PENGUIN BOOKS

Published by the Penguin Group
Penguin Books Ltd, 27 Wrights Lane, London W8 5TZ, England
Penguin Books USA Inc., 375 Hudson Street, New York, New York 10014, USA
Penguin Books Australia Ltd, Ringwood, Victoria, Australia
Penguin Books Canada Ltd, 10 Alcorn Avenue, Toronto, Ontario, Canada M4V 3B2
Penguin Books (NZ) Ltd, 182–190 Wairau Road, Auckland 10, New Zealand

Penguin Books Ltd, Registered Offices: Harmondsworth, Middlesex, England

First published in Penguin Books 1994
10 9 8 7 6 5 4 3 2 1

Typeset by Datix International Limited, Bungay, Suffolk
Printed in England by Clays Ltd, St Ives plc
Set in Monophoto Photina

Dedication

To my family

Who've stuck with me through thick and (relatively) thin.

CONTENTS

Introduction
HOW FAT IS FAT?

If you have ever had a power struggle with a blueberry muffin – and lost – this book is for you. If your mood is determined each day by a glance at the bathroom scales – this book is for you. If you spend more time thinking about food than eating it, believe that your whole life will change when you have reached an 'ideal' weight, and enjoy no peace of mind because you are too *fat* – read on. This book is for you. You may not actually *be* fat – but you *think* fat.

You're not alone. The Western world divides neatly into two camps: natural fatties and natural skinnies. (The former far outnumber the latter.) The groups differ metabolically – and are light years apart *psychologically*. It seems clear that separate body shapes have matching mind-sets – which can be classified as FAT-THINK and THIN-THINK. The key to successful weight loss is learning to trade one for the other.

WHO'S A FATTY?

'Fat' – as every dieter knows – is far more than a physical description. It is also a state of mind. At 5' 4", a

14 stone woman is, by most standards, overweight. But a woman of similar height, accustomed to weighing 8 stone, may perceive herself to be 'fat' if her weight rises to 8½. You know the feeling. Height–weight charts award you a 'normal' score – but old jeans are agonizingly tight. Every evening, when you liberate your constricted tum, it seems to *unfurl* . . . the pattern of your fly deeply imbedded on the front. You are healthy, but somehow uncomfortable. You *feel* fat.

Should you diet? This can be a hard question to answer. There are medical and cosmetic considerations to balance – obsessive behaviour to avoid. In the end, no book can make judgements about 'relative degrees' of fatness. That's *your* job. The following pages make frequent reference to 'fatties' and 'skinnies'. Please note that – for our purposes – 'fatties' are *all those* who wish to lose weight . . . a lot or a little. (Dieters are, as it were, a broad constituency.) Count yourself in or out, as you choose. But rest assured that, if you weigh 8½ stone and you'd rather weigh 8 stone . . . this book is for you.

If – on the other hand – you consider that the desire to be slim is:

1. vain and foolish

2. politically incorrect

3. no laughing matter

then this book is *not* for you. DO NOT read on. You'll probably hate it, and it's bound to annoy you.

1
THE SIZE OF THE PROBLEM

Fatness – or the perception of it – is now a common obsession. Recent UK surveys estimate that *most* British adults – 85 per cent of women, and 60 per cent of men – wish to lose weight. A quarter are actively dieting at any one time. What's more, large numbers are clinically 'obese' (defined as having a body weight 20 per cent above the norm for a particular height). This applies to one woman in eight, and one man in twelve. Comedian Woody Allen once observed that it's easy to tell when a woman is overweight. 'When she lifts her arm,' he pointed out, 'there's another arm underneath.'

By contrast, 'natural skinnies' are the fortunate few. According to doctors, only 5 per cent of the female population – and a slightly higher percentage of men – classify as 'self-regulators'. That's to say that their appetites and metabolisms are balanced in a way which keeps them naturally (and effortlessly) slim. They are different – in the most *fundamental* way – from the rest of us. For a start, they *think* thin. If they have a secret, subliminal preoccupation, it is not about things you can do with Chicken McNuggets.

Nevertheless, **this book is for them, too**, because:

    1. They may have fat friends.

2. We will be probing the skinny mind-set in the interests of research. How can THIN-THINK be adopted by natural fatties for successful weight control?

3. Someday (as skinnies age and their metabolic rates slow) they may *become* fat. **Let's hope so.** It would only be fair.

To fatties, self-regulators are the most enviable of creatures. They enjoy simple but precious freedoms denied to the rest of us. At liberty to follow their inclinations, they eat when they're hungry, and stop when they're full. They choose foods they like, with scant regard for calories or amounts. In short, **they consume without guilt.** It is a fatty's dearest wish to escape the tyranny of the bathroom scales . . . to – just once – satisfy hunger without fear of consequences in the form of flab.

We are left with many questions. For example: is thinness the result of nature or nurture? Are thin people thin because they're *born* with smaller appetites or more efficient metabolisms? Are they *taught* better eating habits? Do they 'naturally' crave low-fat foods? For example: does the average skinny *genetically* prefer carrot sticks to Häagen-Dazs?? (Gimme a break!)

Things Which Fatties Wish to Know About Natural Skinnies

1. What's it like to be truly 'indifferent' to food?

2. Is there something else to think about?

3. Do skinnies experience hunger as we know it?

4. Are their taste buds impaired?

5. How about brain chemistry?

6. Can you be naturally skinny and (at the same time) *fully human*?

Sure, we're jealous. And no wonder. For most of us – that vast, silent (and hungry) majority – fat-fighting is a life-long exercise. And a futile one at that! Research shows that only one dieter in ten achieves lasting success. The rest, doctors say, regain *at least* as much as they lose. Some lose and regain again and again, in a damaging series of 'Yo-Yo' diets. There are people – women in particular – who have been up and down more times than British Airways.

INTERNATIONAL FLAB: HOME AND AWAY

America has problems of even greater proportions. An estimated 100 million adults are in some measure over-weight, and approximately half are on diets. Close to $35 billion (about £20 billion) is spent each year on weight-loss products and services. By contrast, Britain's slimming aids market (including meal replacements and tablets) is worth £2 billion annually.

On both sides of the water, money is clearly being wasted. UK fashion retailers report that fully 50 per cent of all British women take a dress size 16 or over. There is wide regional variation, with small to average sizes selling best in the more affluent (and figure-conscious) South. Edwina Currie's famous indictment of northern diet nearly provoked a civil war . . . but she had a point. Statistics suggest that you're less likely to fit comfortably into an M & S size 8 when you've spent years getting outside a succession of chip butties.

A BRIEF HISTORY OF SKINNINESS

Since large numbers of Western adults – perhaps a majority – are overweight, why is slimness regarded as so desirable? Why, in women, is *extreme* slimness seen as most enviable of all? A review of the last half-century provides some perspective. Fatties should start with *today* and work backwards.

The New Age nineties dawned, looking hopeful for the 'full figured'. It was billed, after all, as a kinder, gentler and more tolerant decade. The well-padded waited, clasping their Slim-Fast, and wondering if, at last, their time had come. Was this to be the decade that spelled the end for the 'human clothes-hanger', bringing with it a broader 'brief' in standards of beauty, and long overdue appreciation for ample proportions? Fat chance!

As it's turned out, things have never been worse for fatties. The unforgiving, 'be-perfect-or-get-lost' eighties passed, leaving behind higher expectations of beauty, fitness and health. Today, it is no longer enough *not to be fat*. It is necessary to be *thin*. Nutritionally 'correct' people stick to low fat diets, and exercise four times a week. Even Barbie dolls are sold to little girls complete with their own workout tapes. Only those over twenty-five can remember when it was considered OK to eat a ham sandwich on white, and then take a nap.

Without doubt, we live in 'fat-ist' times. Our problems began back in the fifties, when Audrey Hepburn emerged as Hollywood's first skinny sex symbol. In an age of curvy stars like Marilyn Monroe and Jane Russell, she looked refreshingly thin and chic. Men felt protective. Women adored her. With hindsight, Audrey was the thin end of the wedge.

Then along came the sixties, and the eventful day when a coltish Twiggy first appeared on the covers of fashion magazines – looking distinctly malnourished. Her knee-bone had a larger circumference than her thigh. This should have set alarm bells ringing for fatties. Ideals of female pulchritude were changing fast. Soon, the emaciation which at first seemed startling would become the norm . . . the standard by which all were to be judged.

Today, we live with the consequences. Every glossy aimed at readers from twelve to seventy proffers pictures of flab-free nymphettes, with concave stomachs and tubular legs. When they stand with their feet together, you can still see daylight between their thighs. Ordinary bangle bracelets slip effortlessly over their elbows, and loosely encircle firm upper arms. *Nothing* wobbles. There is no sign of normal puberty. Every woman yearns to look like them. Even OAPs.

The last half of the twentieth century has been easier on men . . . yet they, too, have been forced to change. Gone are the carefree liquid lunches of yore. Cigarettes are history. New Man grabs a pasta salad with balsamic vinegar and a quick game of squash before returning home to tone his leg muscles on the Stairmaster and watch 'look after your heart' messages on TV.

But, when it comes to bodyshape, nothing has had greater impact than the *seminal* event of the late twentieth century . . . one which has irrevocably changed life for fatties of both sexes. We're talking about:

THE INVENTION OF STRETCH LYCRA

Yes, *Lycra* has *transformed* the fashion industry. To the chagrin of fatties everywhere, these body-revealing garments – originally intended as workout clothes – seem here to stay. Surplus cellulite has no place to hide, as Spandex skirts or bicycle shorts outline bulging tums, and cup mercilessly under drooping bottoms. Lycra flatters the athletic and firm. Supermodels look sensational with bodies wrapped in bandages of (impossibly skimpy) stretchy stuff. Never in the course of human history has there been a more powerful incentive to weight loss. Which raises the twentieth century's *most burning question*:

HOW THIN IS 'THIN ENOUGH'?

There is no simple answer. It's clear that people wish to lose weight for many reasons: medical and cosmetic. While some diet for the sake of their cardio-vascular

ARE YOU A HEALTHY WEIGHT?

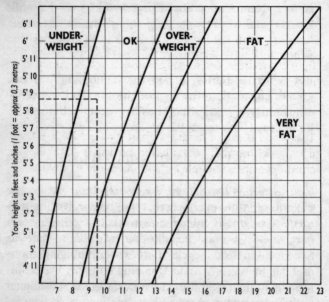

Your height in feet and inches (1 foot = approx 0.3 metres)

UNDER-WEIGHT   OK   OVER-WEIGHT   FAT   VERY FAT

Your weight in stones (1 pound = approx 0.45 kilograms)

UNDERWEIGHT Maybe you need to eat a bit more. But go for well-balanced nutritious foods and don't just fill up on fatty and sugary foods. If you are *very* underweight, see your doctor about it.

OK You're eating the right *quantity* of food but you need to be sure that you're getting a healthy *balance* in your diet.

OVERWEIGHT You should try to lose weight.

FAT You need to lose weight.

VERY FAT You urgently need to lose weight. You would do well to see your doctor, who might refer you to a dietitian.

> ### IF YOU NEED TO LOSE WEIGHT
> Aim to lose 1 or 2 pounds a week until you get down to the 'OK' range. Go for fibre-rich foods and cut down on fat, sugar and alcohol. You'll need to take regular exercise too.

systems, others – women in particular – are driven by an even *greater* imperative. They want to LOOK GOOD IN CLOTHES.

Oh, for a tummy which meets the demands of the skintight black dress. Oh, for thighs which can be confidently exposed in the shortest micro-mini. Oh, for a back which doesn't bulge above and below the bra-line. Oh, for a body on which clothes *cling* well!

The world is full of height–weight charts which set out a range of 'normal' weights for particular heights. The chart opposite is suitable for both men and women:

Most men are content with a score that falls within the 'OK' band. But, not women! They know that official tables *tolerate* moderate plumpness. Lycra dresses do not. There's demand for a better indication of proper height–weight ratio for the 'fashionably thin'. For example: the high-profile model agency Elite says that the average weight of a 5′ 11″ supermodel is 8 stone 6 pounds. Officially, then, she's nearly a stone underweight; maybe two, if you compare her with more 'average' builds. She's 'off the charts' ... but *still upright*.

The conclusion is inescapable. Medical authorities say she's *underweight*. They're lying. She's **sensational**! So, what's needed is a:

Fashionably Thin Woman's 'I Want to Look Good in Clothes' Height–Weight Chart

```
5' 0" = 5 st 10 lb – 6 st 6 lb
5' 1" = 6 st – 6 st 8 lb
5' 2" = 6 st 8 lb – 7 st 3 lb
5' 3" = 7 st – 7 st 7 lb
5' 4" = 7 st 7 lb – 8 st 2 lb
5' 5" = 7 st 10 lb – 8 st 3 lb
5' 6" = 7 st 11 lb – 8 st 6 lb
5' 7" = 8 st – 8 st 8 lb
5' 8" = 8 st 6 lb – 9 st
5' 9" = 8 st 10 lb – 9 st 3 lb
5' 10" = 8 st 11 lb – 9 st 6 lb
5' 11" = 9 st – 9 st 8 lb
6' 0" = 9 st 4 lb – 10 st
```

These weights will place you on the official borderline between 'underweight' and 'normal'. In other words, fashionably slim – but not emaciated. If they appear a bit brutal, they are at least a broad target for those who want bodies like Yasmin Le Bon's. (No doubt she weighs less than we've allowed here.) So, set aside all thoughts about being 'big boned' for your height. Notice the generous 8 to 10 pounds tolerance at each height-level for those who claim to be extra heavy on:

1. bone mass

2. muscle

3. grey matter.

After all, how much more pelvis, pectoral or frontal lobe can you have than the *rest* of the human race? The harsh truth is that few things – apart from *fat* – can account for additional pounds. Unless you have, say, floor-length hair or plutonium fillings.

Many will point out that there's no *need* to look like a supermodel. The idea is to maintain a reasonable, healthy weight. It's unnecessary – even undesirable – to appear 'skinny'. But for women of most ages, this comforting argument is flawed. On every billboard, in every magazine and on TV, the female beauties against whom we judge ourselves are THIN. *Very* thin. Many's the cover girl who – at 6 foot or so – weighs in at a sylph-like 8 stone 7 pounds. Late twentieth century fashion in general – and Lycra in particular – have imposed on women a new and unwelcome obligation: designer starvation.

Anyway, if you wish to emulate the Christy Turlingtons and Cindy Crawfords of this world (and who doesn't?) the above chart is useful. There's thin, and *thin*. It's best to understand, going in, what you're asking of yourself.

MAN'S WORLD

The usual 'double standard' applies when it comes to body shape, and nutrition. Men experience fewer problems with height–weight charts, and fewer traumas altogether about 'degrees' of slimness. With rare exceptions, they do *not* go through life longing to look emaciated, like Gandhi. Quite the reverse. Skinny young men are haunted by the spectre of the '7 stone weakling', fearing that Arnold Schwarzenegger types will kick sand in their faces, and embarrass them in front of girls. Yes, men like to have hard, flat stomachs and slim hips . . . but to be otherwise muscular, and well-built. *Above all*, they want to have bodies which **look good to other men when they undress in locker rooms**. Few go through life wishing to appear cadaverous in clothes.

Without doubt, we tolerate a far wider variety of male body shapes than female. Think, for example, of film stars. Unless their physiques are exaggerated (like Schwarzenegger's or Danny De Vito's) they're scarcely noticed. OK, few celluloid heart-throbs have pot bellies and double chins – though the Bridges brothers looked fairly 'slack' in *The Fabulous Baker Boys*. (Michelle Pfeiffer, on the other hand, appeared to be chiselled from flint.) But, Hollywood's most bankable men – Harrison

Ford, Tom Cruise and Kevin Costner – are sexy, appealing and *normal*. Their ribs do not protrude. They appear to be taking nourishment. Few fans watching the bedroom scenes in *Pretty Woman* knew or cared whether Richard Gere looked *thin*. Everyone noticed that Julia Roberts did.

By nature, the female body carries a higher percentage of fat than the male. Around 20 to 25 per cent of a woman's body mass is composed of fat, as compared with 10 to 15 per cent of a man's. Variations in where and how fat is deposited account for many of the characteristics which we perceive as 'maleness' or 'femaleness'. Sometimes, young women who diet too strenuously are suspected of wishing to somehow neutralize their femininity by assuming a more androgynous shape. Furthermore, there is evidence that too *low* a level of female body fat can depress fertility.

It's easy to see that fashion-conscious Western women are caught in a trap. To achieve contemporary standards of beauty, we are called upon to diet away our distinguishing features. Hips, for example. And bottoms. In short – to work against the very nature of femininity. This is not to suggest that we're all meant to look like Roseanne Barr. But few of us are cut out to resemble Iman, either.

Those of us who long to imitate the lean, mean body shapes of supermodels who grace the pages of *Vogue* and *Elle* – or Hollywood's most admired females – have our work cut out. (Not to mention our desserts.) This is a mammoth task, requiring sustained effort and personal commitment. Especially for the over twenty-fives.

Remember that star-ettes like Cher and Madonna regularly work out for three to four hours a day with personal trainers named 'Dimitri' or 'Josh' ... pausing only to devour a teaspoonful of vitamin-rich lemon grass and herbal tea.

So, **why should we do it?**

DIET AS DESTINY

It isn't fair? You bet it isn't. Because the requirement to be very thin in order to be perceived as beautiful is now part of being female. It goes with the territory, and cannot be ignored. Women – excepting the fortunate 5 per cent – must diet. Worse still, they must do so far more rigorously than men if they are to achieve the disciplined body shapes which nineties taste requires – and with which they themselves can be content.

The last part is the important bit. It explains why – though we rattle our cages – it is difficult to escape. We have been 'got at'.

Small wonder that bitter resentment has now fuelled an anti-diet backlash. Today's women are often counselled to 'stop starving and come to terms with their "natural" weight'. We're reminded that the desire for extreme slimness is imposed on us from *outside* ... by men, perhaps, or the fashion industry. Dieting is a metaphor for the 'subordination' of women. We're not *fat*. We're victims of external pressure.

How true. So what? The fact is that such pressures exist – and, for most women, they're a feature of modern life … impossible to ignore. Understanding the problem gives us no real defence; the urge for beauty, health and desirability in the form of slimness persists. For better or (many would argue) worse, we have internalized the message. Today, the real pressure comes from *within*. The best course of action is to learn how to manage it.

For many thousands of women, then, the course of least resistance – and, ultimately, greatest happiness – is to give in. Yes, women (and many men) must *diet*. It is their destiny. Pointless to apportion blame, bemoan the human condition or rend your (outsize) garments. Fruitless to concoct elaborate conspiracy theories. Even worse to imagine that there are alternative choices. There are not.

The consolation is that, if we work hard, some of us will diet effectively. We will lose weight, and *keep it off*. But, a successful transformation demands more than a simple cut in calories and saturated fats. The trick is to learn to reprogramme *attitudes* along with *eating habits* … to master a new 'mind-set' which turns years of FAT-THINK into THIN-THINK. We're talking fundamental change in philosophy here. Wimps need not apply.

So, if you are seeking a 'quick fix' – a sure-fire formula for combining foods (only puree of pineapple 'til 4 p.m., then lentils) which promises to burn calories and magically shed pounds – read no further. This book offers no nutritional miracles. (Nothing, at any rate, that you can whip up in a food processor.) There is no 'magic bullet' … unless you count will-power. Sensible eating – plus a shift in attitudes and behaviour – is suggested here.

Above all, wannabe skinnies must shed a common misconception about diets. There is simply no such thing as a super-diet which can be followed for a bit, and then – when desired weight loss has been achieved – discarded. Here is the SINGLE MOST IMPORTANT (and depressing) thing to know about effective diets –

THE FIRST PRINCIPLE OF THIN-THINK
DIETS ARE NEVER 'OVER'

The change in habits is not temporary. Like diamonds, 'Diets are Forever'. For most people, carefully modified eating must become a permanent way of life. Hard luck.

Does this mean a lifetime of controlled deprivation? Sssort of. (Except that you can't think of it in those terms ... of which, more later.) The point is that – unless you're one of nature's lucky handful of self-regulators – you've got to be fairly determined in order to doggedly remain slim through life's trials, traumas and hormone changes.

Concerned about the risks and dangers of long-term 'compulsive' starvation? A light-hearted look at what makes fatties and skinnies tick may set your mind at rest. It will certainly remind you that you're not alone. Despite present anxieties, there is still a great deal of difference between an effective diet and an 'eating disorder'. Wishing to be a stone lighter – and taking sensible action – does not make you an anorexic waiting to happen.

'Everything in moderation', then? Yes – but determined dieters deserve more than a pat on the head, and a few kind clichés from the local GP. The truth is that figure control requires years of valiant and sustained effort. There's nothing 'moderate' about it. Dieters are often surprised (and defeated) by the sheer tenacity needed to shed even one stubborn pound. Many – women in particular – give up. Defeated, they shake off the yoke of an austere existence. 'I will,' they resolve, 'stop dieting. I will come to terms with my *natural* body weight.'

But, few find real peace of mind. They are ever aware of a lingering aspiration, left unfulfilled. Unfair it may be ... imposed from the outside it may be. The conclusion, however, is clear. **You may as well diet**. It's less miserable to *lose* the weight than to spend the best years of your life hating yourself for *not* losing it.

2

HOW TO TELL IF YOU'RE A 'NATURAL' FATTY OR 'NATURAL' SKINNY

Thirty Unmistakable Signs

Fat – as all dieters know – is far more than a physical condition. It is also possible to be *spiritually* fat. That's what's meant by FAT-THINK.

A trim body does not guarantee a matching mind-set. In many cases, psyche and body weight are directly at odds. We all know that you can be *fat* and think fat . . . be *slim* and think *fat* . . . or lose weight, *become thin*, and *still* think fat. Fat-heads (and that includes most of us) are easy to spot. They have a characteristic attitude towards food, and approach to eating. If in doubt about where *you* fit, consult the following tables. Remember that, point for point, there are lots of natural fatties in the world, while natural skinnies are (comparatively) thin on the ground.

All this serves a purpose. Dieters are more likely to enjoy long-term success in achieving and maintaining slim figures if they can align mind-set more closely with desired body shape. Anyway, before 'going to work' on yourself in a fundamental way, it helps to know what you're dealing with.

Thirty Signs That You're a 'Natural Fatty'

1. Eating is – quite simply – your favourite activity. You needn't be hungry. Food is, for you, a form of recreation.

2. You like nearly every part of nearly every food. When you eat meat, you also enjoy the gristle.

3. You gnaw happily on bones when food is gone, stripping them bare.

4. You cannot understand why others reject food which is 'greasy'. This does not diminish its appeal.

5. You seldom lose your appetite or refuse food – even when sick.

6. You are baffled when others declare themselves 'too tired to eat'.

7. Even at times of crisis, food is never far from your thoughts.

8. When you wake in the morning, you automatically review what you ate *yesterday* – and plan what to eat *today*.

9. When things are going badly, you console yourself with food.

10. When things are going well, you reward yourself with food.

11. When a dreamy new lover suggests *skipping dinner* and going straight to bed – you experience a pang of disappointment.

12. You prefer to eat *alone*. Food is best enjoyed without interruption or conversation.

13. Sometimes – when no one's looking – you abandon good manners, and *shovel* food in.

14. For you, food is the focal point of any social occasion. When invited to 'a show and dinner', you sit through the show, impatient for dinner.

15. If business meetings run through lunch, you become edgy. A missed meal is a deal-breaker.

16. You like food in *any* condition . . . hot, cold, day-old, stale – or congealed.

17. You salt *all* food before eating, without first tasting it. You have been known to surreptitiously salt bread.
    You have been tempted to salt toothpaste.

18. Even when *full*, adding extra seasoning to food increases your capacity.

19. No matter how large the helping on your plate, you *finish it all*. You often match appetite to portion-size . . . not the other way around.

20. When alone, you lick the plate or put your fingers in it to mop up the last crumbs or grains of salt.

21. Certain activities are an automatic 'cue' to eat. You always eat while watching telly, paying bills or having a hot drink. Hunger has nothing to do with it.

22. When enjoying the taste of food, you can consume unlimited amounts.

23. Even the 'formation' of food fascinates you. You often put a piece of something in your mouth simply because you like the colour or shape. You specially like 'burnt bits'.

24. You revel in sight, smell and texture. Eating is, for you, a 'total' sensual experience.

25. You may exercise great restraint – but you naturally prefer rich or 'fattening' foods. (A celery stalk filled with cream cheese is of interest only for the cream cheese.)

26. You cannot rest while a single morsel of a food you love remains in the refrigerator or on your plate. Or on someone *else's* plate.

27. You *never* skip a meal. Faced with global catastrophe (the outbreak of nuclear war), you'd find time to grab lunch.

28. Food seldom (if ever) 'disagrees' with you.

29. When offered 'seconds' of food you actually *dislike* – you happily accept.

30. In company, there is nothing you secretly hate more than *giving away bites*.

Thirty Signs That You're a 'Natural' Skinny

1. You resent the amount of *time* eating takes.

2. You regard food as an obligation and necessity, rather than a pleasure.

3. You skip regular meals unless reminded, and often 'forget' to eat.

4. Preparing food is a bore. When hungry, you prefer to 'grab something easy'. Often, something in a wrapper, which can be purchased from a newsagent.

5. You seldom season food to 'improve' it. You're not interested enough.

6. You'll consent to eat only a limited number of favourite items, drawn from *one* food group: junk.

7. As part of the legacy of your childhood, you enjoy eating most when *coaxed*.

8. Food is power. You know how to use it to manipulate other people. (You're in a strong position, since you don't need it.)

9. You cannot understand other people's obsession with something as *mundane* as food. It's like having a fixation about laundry.

10. You sometimes like the *taste* of foods, but are 'put off' by other characteristics. You may object to the texture or 'mouth feel' (for example, avocados). Fatties are oblivious to such considerations. They swallow too fast to notice.

11. You prefer food which 'goes down easily'. You can't be bothered to chew.

12. You do not regard food as the centre-piece of social encounters. You are pleased to join friends for 'a film and a curry' . . . but the real attraction is the film.

13. You can't eat *at all* when you're upset, ill or worried.

14. When all's well, there are a zillion things you'd rather do than 'feed your face'.

15. You do *not* head 'straight for the fridge':
    a. when you arrive home from work
    b. during TV commercials.

16. You rarely experience overwhelming *hunger* as fatties know it. When you do, it is satisfied in two bites.

17. You have never experienced a 'stuffed' feeling, since you stop eating at the first opportunity.

18. Feeling 'too full' (which happens on the third bite) makes you nauseous.

19. Whingeing dieters (and there are many!) *also* upset your stomach.

20. Anyway, why do people object to carrying a little extra weight? (You wish you could gain some.)

21. You're easily 'put off' by food. You will reject a whole meal if one vegetable looks 'dodgy' or the meat is too rare.

22. You have a small capacity. You're skilled at pushing unwanted food around the plate, and burying it under the decorative garnish.

23. Since childhood, you've had 'allergic' reactions to food. You come up in a rash when forced to eat *anything* you don't care for. (When you were small, this included all food except Smarties and crisps.)
    (Fatties *never* suffer from food allergies. All foods agree with them.)

24. It's more entertaining to feed food to pets than to eat it yourself.

25. You fidget a lot. Friends complain that you never sit still. Somehow, you seem to keep moving even while seated at the dinner table.

26. You don't mind a bit when others take 'bites' of your food. (You're grateful for the help.)

27. At restaurants, you often complain that portions are 'too big'. Just *seeing* quantities of food on your plate fills you with a sense of obligation, and spoils your appetite.

Dog as diet buddy:

(OMELETTE À 'LE SPANIEL')

This *never* happens to fatties, who rejoice when large amounts are placed before them.

28. Free to eat whatever you like, you irritate friends by displaying indifference to foods others would kill for. Like cheesecake.

29. On occasion, you eat lots without really noticing. But you *never gain weight*. This is because you do not pay sufficient *attention* to food. Wounded by your indifference, the calories you ignore slip straight through your system, instead of hanging around in the form of fat cells.

30. You are relieved when meals are *over*, so that you can get on with the 'real' business of life. To fatties, food *is* the 'real' business of life.

NOTE

Skinnies should beware the down side of being a naturally thin person. With no experience of the gastronomic self-control so familiar to fatties, there's every risk you'll *become fat* as you grow older, and metabolism slows.

We all hope so.

Having gained pounds, it will be hard for you to lose them, since you have failed to acquire the skills and habits of weight management.

Who cares?

The way we fatties see it, you've had about forty good years.

And finally . . .

ONE SURE SIGN THAT YOU'RE A 'BORN AGAIN' SKINNY (OR FORMER FATTY):

Despite acquiring svelte shapes, 'Born Again' skinnies retain all the *psychological* characteristics of natural fatties . . . but add one more:

THEY BECOME HARDLINE 'FATISTS'.

Neo-skinnies show no tolerance for unreconstructed porkers, believing that 'if I can do it, so can he'. Or, 'I suffered – so should she!' The fear and self-loathing once inwardly directed lock onto a new target.

'Born Agains' refuse to hire fat people. They do not choose fat friends. They lecture anyone who will listen on the perils of cholesterol and the advantages of diet. The sight of an unrepentant and self-indulgent fatty fills them with fury. (They itch to snatch cream buns from well-padded fists.) They are reminded – too painfully – of their own personal demons. In short, 'Born Again' skinnies display an acute *fear of fat*. They become F A T - O - P H O B I C.

3
FEAR OF DIETS
'I Can't Cope with Food'

Diet. It doesn't sound bad on paper, right? Just cut out a few of your favourite things (sweets, for example, and fried foods), eliminate booze, blunt any hunger-pangs with the odd carrot stick, and a few weeks later – hey, presto. Move over, Jerry Hall.

Why, then, is the failure-rate so high? Why do experts claim that only *one dieter in ten* successfully reaches his or her 'target' weight ... and maintains it thereafter? Why do more women than men allow body weight to climb until they classify as 'obese'?

Doctors and other professionals warn that, these days, more people appear to be 'losing control' of eating habits. Both sexes are affected – but studies show that women are at greater risk than men. It seems we have lost the ability to eat 'normally' ... to balance what we consume with actual physical *need*. Our relationship with food is often distorted. We use it to punish or console ourselves ... to deal with crises or establish 'control' over life. We eat for many reasons – apart from the simple (and pleasant) satisfaction of hunger. There is no hurt so great that it cannot be relieved by the direct application of a cup-cake.

The conclusion is that *food* is probably the most commonly abused substance of all; the only one which is both a necessity and an addiction. You *gotta* have it, but you *shouldn't* have it. In short, we can't handle it. Most women stand a better chance of forming a stable, long-term relationship with Warren Beatty than with lunch.

DEMAND FEEDING

Many fatties experience conflicts about food *early* in life (at roughly the time they begin taking solids) and never outgrow them. For the next seven or eight decades, they remain preoccupied with body weight, shape and size. At the heart of all this is *eating* – never far from the forefront of their thoughts. For example:

FAT-THINK

1. What have I eaten so far today?

2. How soon can I eat again?

3. I want the burger, but I *should* choose the salad.

4. I want the French dressing, but I *should* leave it off.

5. I could murder a chocolate milkshake.

6. Do I look thinner, yet?

THIN-THINK

1. Lovely morning.

2. Breakfast time!

3. Hope I've got a clean shirt.

4. Seems there's no solution to the crisis in the Middle East.

5. Think I feel a bit peckish.

6. Oh, look. Interest rates are up again.

If you naturally *think fat*, only a handful of things will push food – even temporarily – from your mind. A pools win, for example. Or the outbreak of nuclear war. In fact, even *that* is uncertain. Comedienne Joan Rivers once considered what she'd do if told that *the Bomb* would drop in ten minutes. 'Waiter!' she shouted. 'Another plate of fettucini!'

The trouble is that FAT-THINK is as monotonous as it is self-defeating. Time and again, we resolve to eat small amounts of 'healthy' low-fat foods, then pack away truck-loads of calorie-laden junk. There's a magic weight we'd like to be, believing that it would bring contentment. But we seldom achieve it ... and if, by chance, we do, it proves nearly impossible to maintain. We are scuppered by hunger, self-pity – or pre-menstrual water retention.

Such frustrations prompted comedienne Rita Rudner to devise a 'foolproof' method for maintaining the ideal weight. 'Every morning,' she explains, 'I hang from the shower rod, and lower myself *slowly* onto the bathroom scale. When I reach the weight I want to be . . . I black out.'

When a fatty's life is out of control, so – very often – is weight. (Or, maybe it's the reverse.) Either way, it's crystal clear that so-called 'comfort eating' produces, in the long term, quite the opposite effect. The soothing intake of fats, the satisfying 'sugar rush' soon pile on pounds, deepening any crisis, and increasing recovery-time. It's a vicious circle, reflected in FAT-THINK.

When, for example, a lover goes AWOL, here's what happens:

FAT-THINK

Good grief, I'm so depressed!

I owe myself some consolation. A chocolate biscuit.

Hello, mirror. Hello, fatso. Hello, *spotty* fatso.

No wonder he doesn't love me. Who could? Who ever *will*?

Good grief, I'm so depressed.

Pass the chocolate biscuits.

THIN-THINK

Good grief, I'm so depressed!

I owe myself some little pleasure. I always wanted to be *blonde*.

Sign me up for two sessions of aerobics, and one of California stretch.

I'll take the cute leopard-print leotard.

He'll be sorry. I am gonna be so gorgeous . . .

Pass the mineral water.

Yes, when self-confidence takes a knock, any normal woman reaches for the biscuit tin. But, this is no time for self-inflicted injury! Better to vent pent-up emotions on the nearest rowing machine or exer-cycle. Meanwhile, do something *positive* with your biscuit tin. Throw it at him.

REMEMBER
Never in the course of human history has anyone managed to eat unhappiness away.

Rhoda – heroine of the popular MTM sitcom of the same name – once tried to cope with the trauma of divorce by chewing on a Mars Bar. 'I don't know why I bother to eat this,' she reflected gloomily. 'I could just apply it directly to my hips.'

NAKED TRUTH

Here's what they *don't* tell you as you embark hopefully on the Cambridge/Rotation Plan/Slim-Fast diet, or purchase your Philadelphia Light. *Diet* – whether it's undertaken to lose or maintain weight – requires reserves of self-discipline, and considerable will-power. Food restriction is *uncomfortable*. (Where does it say that on the Optifast box?)

For natural fatties who wish to stay slim, some form of restricted eating must become a way of life. A return to 'normal' intake (the kind that first made you heavier than you want to be) is not on. DIETS ARE NEVER OVER. Fatties must come to terms with that.

Is it all worth the effort? You bet. First, there are sound medical reasons for being slim, and compelling cosmetic ones. The plain fact is that the quality of the average person's life improves when he or she is slim. Even a few surplus pounds can have an adverse effect. If in doubt, try carrying an 8 to 10 pound baby (or bag of groceries) up two flights of steps. Then pretend that you can't put it down. Ever.

For women in particular, being slim seems worthwhile. They report feeling better in clothes, more confident with members of the opposite sex, and – in general – happier with themselves. But, the *best* thing about achieving a target weight is that it allows you to put preoccupation with body shape on the back burner (a slow, steady simmer) while you get on with the rest of your life.

This is no cue for fatties to self-destruct or hurl themselves under their chocolate wagon wheels. Even if you have tried many times to diet – and failed – all is not lost. The secret is to modify your attitudes along with your eating habits. You *can* become slim. You *can* stay that way. You needn't be a hero(ine) or paragon. Most diets fail because people *don't know how* to diet. They're uncomfortable, and can't cope. They're not entirely sure they *want* to diet. They lack a co-ordinated physical and mental approach. They are certainly not prepared – either physically or psychologically – for restricted food intake. The first hurdle to overcome, therefore, is:

FEAR OF DIETS

Many people approach diets with the same sense of dread as a trip to the dentist. 'This,' they warn them-selves, 'is going to hurt.' The only uncertainty is *how much*. Wannabe skinnies are tense from the start; fearful, vulnerable, jumpy. In this frame of mind, they are easily defeated. Small wonder that many surrender at the first sign of hardship.

FAT-THINK

I can't eat the Birdseye lemon mousse?
OK. I give in.

The first step towards THIN-THINK is to confront *fear of diets*. There are comparisons to be drawn with childbirth. In both cases, you're surprised by the pain. Somehow caught off-guard ... unprepared. You wonder whether it 'hurts this much for everyone'. You begin to believe that there's something unusual – abnormal, even – about your case. Ability to endure is undermined by doubt. You are now a victim of pain; reactive instead of 'in charge'.

Therefore, for the avoidance of doubt, here is the *second* most important thing to know about diets –

THE SECOND PRINCIPLE OF THIN-THINK
DIETS ARE HELL
(*They are hell for everyone.*)

The *bad* news is that it is impossible to diet painlessly ... blissfully unaware that life has changed. There is, however, some *good* news. Unlike being at the dentist's or in labour, *you* are in control of the pain. You can make it stop or simply 'turn down the volume' at any time, because you are in charge. Understanding this can build confidence, help you to relax, and raise your threshold of tolerance.

Unless you have serious medical problems (or are under a doctor's supervision) you should not plunge headlong into a Spartan regime. Instead, develop your diet *gradually* ... one step at a time. Toe in the water first – then total immersion. Today, trade your customary morning croissant for a slice of wholemeal toast. Tomorrow, eat the toast without butter. When you're ready, try drinking your coffee or tea with a splash of skimmed milk instead of semi-skimmed. Then, cut out the sugar. Before you know it, you're eating a diet-friendly breakfast which doesn't scare the wits out of you. You can handle it. Not only do you feel virtuous ... but really *butch*. Self-esteem gets an enormous boost. You've taken the first important step in exchanging FAT-THINK for the new mind-set called THIN-THINK.

In order to make the transition complete, you'll *also* need to develop:

1. confidence

2. an ability to relax

3. a sense of humour

4. a large supply of mineral water.

Have them close at hand as you read the following chapters.

4
THIN-THINK – PREPARING THE MIND

There was a time – not so many years ago – when, if you wanted to lose weight, you'd pick the ham from your sandwich (still coated in excess mayo) and eat it – leaving aside the bread, which was 'fattening'. Meat, experts assured us, was 'protein'. *Starch* was the culprit . . . but protein was OK. It would be hard to be wronger. Experts, in other words, blew it.

In those days (circa fifties and sixties), no other foodstuff was as much maligned as the poor old potato. Potatoes, bread, pasta and desserts were to be avoided at all costs. It was not until the revolution in nutritional thinking (which seemed to take place during the seventies) that 'starches' – now restyled 'complex carbohydrates' – were rehabilitated. Potatoes enjoyed a long overdue moment in the sun. They were acknowledged to be high in desirable vitamin C, and low in harmful fats . . . as long as you baked, boiled or steamed them, and didn't add banned substances like butter.

Today's new *'bête noire'* is *saturated fat* – the type found in red meats, eggs and dairy products. These days, if the milkman leaves bottles of full cream milk on your door-step, you worry about what the neighbours will think. You dare not purchase sausages during daylight hours.

Instead, the foodstuff of choice is *fibre* – which would-be skinnies (and, for that matter, would-be healthies) should embrace. Who would have thought, just a few short decades ago, that it was possible to have strong feelings about a bowl of All-Bran? (No prizes for pointing out that many have strong feelings *after* a bowl of All-Bran.)

One thing you have to say for the last two decades: the health-education message has come through loud and clear. (Perhaps it's the medical profession's way of atoning for the fiasco last time.) Unless you've been living under the proverbial rock, you will by now be aware of the main rules for healthy eating and sensible weight loss. We needn't, therefore, belabour them here, save to highlight one salient point. This is something which doctors won't point out, but every dieter *instinctively* knows. It has nothing to do with nutritional science, and everything to do with psychology:

THE THIRD PRINCIPLE OF THIN-THINK
IF YOU ARE EATING IT AND ENJOYING IT,
YOU ARE PROBABLY DOING SOMETHING
WRONG.

Ask professional advice on weight loss, and experts will insist that 'diet' foods – low-fat, low-sodium – *can* be enjoyable. But they don't say *compared to what*. Compared to being pegged out in the Mojave Desert in August – maybe. Compared to getting outside a piece of cheesecake – no way.

I have yet to meet the weightwatcher – fat or slim – who will, hand on heart, claim to prefer a slice of dry breakfast toast to one sporting a pat of melted butter.

One of the biggest hurdles to cross on the way from FAT-THINK to THIN-THINK is to change your *concept* of 'enjoyment'. We all believe we are entitled to enjoy the food we eat, and that meal choices should be made on that basis. Wrong! This is a luxury which aspiring skinnies cannot afford. Successful dieters must *rethink* the link between food and enjoyment. Goodbye, instant gratification. A higher form of (long-term) pleasure should be your goal.

Imagine, for example, this scenario. You've been 'good' all day, kept calories low, and worked up quite an appetite for dinner. You've decided on salad, but feel disappointed at the idea of having to eat it lightly sprinkled with lemon juice when you'd prefer creamy blue cheese dressing served by the ladle.

FAT-THINK

Why waste a perfectly good appetite on something miserable and watery?

I want something more satisfying.

Anyway, I've been good all day.

We're all entitled to a little *enjoyment*. That's what life's about, isn't it?

Granny fried everything, and lived to be ninety-three.

THIN-THINK

Boring old salad with lemon juice.

I'll put baby corn-cobs and raw mushroom on top for more 'pizazz'.

By tomorrow, it won't matter whether I enjoyed it a lot or a little. Dinner will be 'history'.

But my tummy will be *flatter*.

I am gonna enjoy wearing my short skirt – all day!

Would-be skinnies must master the trick of *deferring* pleasure. Not eliminating, but deferring. That dollop of blue cheese will, of course, provide a few moments of bliss. Then it will be over . . . but the legacy will remain. You will feel *fat*. This will make you unhappy, and undermine your efforts. You will resolve to diet even more stringently tomorrow in order to make up lost ground. You will probably fail.

The trick to thinking thin is to set aside the notion that you are entitled to full satisfaction every time you sit down to eat. Those who successfully become slim – and stay that way – learn to choose foods which *do the least damage* while assuaging hunger. They are able to swap instant gratification for long-term advantage. Inner strength comes from the thought of even *greater* pleasure to come: the extra energy they'll feel, the admiration they'll attract as surplus pounds melt away. Serious dieters sacrifice an insignificant bit of the *present* for a long stretch of *future*. They know that a five-minute wallow in the creamy blue cheese does not compare with the enduring joy of having a body with *outlines*.

Of course, every aspiring skinny needs to assemble a bag of psychological 'tricks' for getting past moments of maximum temptation. For example: a colleague at work has a birthday, and you're offered a slice of cake. Muster the words 'no, thanks!' and – after the initial disappointment – you'll feel a sense of *relief*. Once the decision is made, the 'crisis' is over. Breaking a diet is a little like hitting someone in anger. It feels great for a moment – and rotten for a long time.

It's an unfortunate fact that losing weight means eating to live . . . and not the other way around. You should be prepared to find most recommended foods short on enjoyment. Let's face it – no person in his or her right mind prefers a breakfast of sodium-free oat bran to eggs, bacon and waffles. But, for natural fatties, life is a trade-off. **You are**, in other words, **what you *don't* eat.**

THE FATTIES' PLEASURE PRINCIPLE:
Hi-cal food you adore is over in minutes.
The resulting flab isn't.

5

WHAT TO EAT

A Short Guide to THIN-THINK

Fatties can be forgiven for concluding that – these days – *dieting* requires a Ph. D. in nutrition. It's no longer enough, it seems, simply to *eat less*. You should know your proteins from your complex carbohydrates, your saturates from your polyunsaturates, your kilojoules from your calories. Not to mention E numbers, preservatives, cholesterol ('good' and 'bad'), sucrose and sodium. Supermarket shopping takes hours longer, as you stop to decipher the labels on tins.

Moreover, there's the vexed question of *which* diet to follow. Choose from F-Plan, Rotation, Hip and Thigh, Weight Watchers, Pritikin, Scarsdale, Mayo Clinic or Pineapple (the fruit, not the dancewear). The list is endless. You can drink your calories in the form of a synthetic milkshake 'meal replacement' – or test various theories about 'combination eating'. Provided you have the fortitude to consume nothing but kiwi fruit with your pilchards.

Better, perhaps, to keep things simple. There's nothing specially *mysterious* about diet. In brief: you need to *cut down* on calories and saturated fats – and probably to *increase* exercise. You need a *little* common sense, and *lots* of will-power. The only other thing you need is:

The Seven Rules of THIN-THINK

1. CUT OUT AS MUCH AS POSSIBLE OF THE FOLLOWING:

    a. fat

    b. sugar

    c. salt.

Adequate amounts of *all three* occur naturally in a balanced, low-fat diet. There is no need to add any extra. For example: anyone who imagines they'll need salt tablets if they stop adding salt to food is wrong (or living in the Kalahari Desert).

2. EAT MORE FIBRE-RICH FOODS

Fibre – of which most people on weight-loss diets should actually eat *more* – is the name for a special group of carbohydrates. Included in the category are: wholemeal bread and pasta, potatoes, rice (brown is best), cereals, beans, vegetables and fruit. Fibre helps everything. It provides 'bulk' to make you feel full without adding too many calories, and contains vitamins for good health. It is vital to regularity (which certainly makes you *feel* thinner).

Fibre is found only in foods which grow from the ground – or are composed of them. There are plenty of fibre-rich foods to choose from. Some of the strong contenders are: dried apricots, potatoes (with their skins), red kidney beans, spinach, baked beans, peas, sweetcorn, unsugared muesli and the two staple wholemeals – pasta and bread. (This definitely leaves out Dove Bars and Burger King Frostees). Plain bread is, in fact, one of the best fillers there is when you're hungry. The catch is that you can't butter it. No, *not even* a low-fat spread, which still contains fats and calories *which are not needed*, and can be easily eliminated. (Efficient weight loss requires ruthless pruning.) The truth is that plain, fresh wholemeal bread tastes just fine on its own, once you get used to the idea. It doesn't need much help.

At snack-time, accompany your slice with a sugarless hot drink (tea, herbal tea or coffee with skimmed milk) for a reasonably full and satisfied feeling. OK, it's not the same as hot, buttered scones and cocoa, but let's not quibble. It's *something to eat*! You know you're thinking thin when you actually begin to look forward to your rations.

3. THINK GREEN

Dieters who continue to *think fat* often reject fruit and vegetables on the grounds that they're 'boring'. They are, however, a key source of essential fibre. Experience teaches that successful weight loss is directly linked to willingness to *fill up* on fruit and vegetables. After all . . . what else is there? Aspiring skinnies will already be hitting the bread and cereal products hard. Fats and sugars are out. 'Animal protein' (i.e., lean meat, chicken and fish) must be eaten in limited quantities. Rule out fruit and veg, and there's very little left to throw at a hunger-pang.

Sprout-o-Phobia

For reasons that baffle the rest of the world, many Brits are 'uncomfortable' with fruit and vegetables. They don't understand them very well, and – when at supermarkets – often pay good money for melons too hard to eat or bruised brown bananas. Government surveys show that fewer than a quarter of British adults eat fresh citrus fruit once a week. Only half have an apple or pear. Nevertheless, these foods are essential to any weight-loss or weight-maintenance programme – and fundamental to health.

Experts speculate that the relative absence of fruit and veg from the British diet (especially in Scotland) is one reason for the nation's high rate of heart disease. It now appears that it's not only what you *take out* of a diet which accounts for efficient weight loss and good health . . . it's also what you *put in*.

Reasons Why Brits Avoid Fruits and Vegetables:

   a. They'd rather eat chips.
   b. The only fruits with which they're familiar are tasteless apples, imported oranges, and a few rock-hard pears.
   c. Their mothers boiled all vegetables for *hours*, to make sure they were dead.
   d. They'd rather eat chips.

Fatties take note: to O.D. on fruit and veg is not a *penance*. Today's supermarkets are full of fab produce. If you don't like peaches, plums, nectarines or melon, there is something fairly strange about you. Summer watermelon contains so few calories that it scarcely qualifies as food. Have a *big* slice! Fresh, sweet pineapple is also diet-friendly, and an excellent choice. It's what the gods gave fatties in exchange for dessert.

In order to make cooked vegetables more interesting (and to retain vitamins) *do not* immerse them in water. Instead, steam them for a few minutes, so that they remain crisp and fairly crunchy. (You know you've overdone it if broccoli stalks wind easily around a fork, or sway in the breeze.) For added interest, try steaming a few novelty items like baby corn-cobs, mange-tout or new potatoes in their skins. Some people claim that stir-frying vegetables is a good idea for dieters . . . but maybe it's best not to risk it. (Fate has a way of striking back at fatties who fry.)

4. SPUDS-YOU-LIKE

Don't be afraid to make the most of potatoes. Innocent spuds spent years in the nutritional wilderness, unjustly condemned as 'fattening'. We now know that the only thing wrong with potatoes is the fat commonly added to them. Chips are often cooked in fat and are therefore high in calories. But the spud in its *natural* state is a dieter's delight: high in fibre and vitamin C, low in fats.

Since much desirable fibre is in the skins, jacket potatoes are a good choice. If you wash them, then wrap carefully in foil before baking, skins won't become leathery. *Do not* top spuds with butter, margarine, grated cheese or sour cream. Eat plain or sprinkled with fresh herbs or chives, or add a tablespoon of very low fat plain yogurt.

5. DON'T SABOTAGE YOUR OWN DIET

Once you've formed the habit of including plenty of fruit and vegetables in your diet, beware of destroying the positive effect.

Things NOT to Do to Fruit and Vegetables:

a. Add butter or other fats to potatoes and hot vegetables.

b. Drown your salad in oily or creamy dressings, or mayonnaise. (Try a sprinkling of lemon juice, or balsamic vinegar.)

c. Fry or sauté your potatoes. Or roast them in tins where they can absorb juices or fat from meats.

d. Eat your fresh fruit salad topped with cream.

e. Liberally add avocado or shellfish (shrimp, lobster, crab, prawns) to a salad. (All are deceptively high in cholesterol.)

f. Use garnishes which are high in calories – like croutons or bacon bits. Olives (green or black) should be eaten sparingly. Limit yourself to one or two.

g. Snack on nuts. Nourishing, and plenty of fibre – but high in calories. One packet of salted peanuts will poleaxe your diet for the day. Nuts to that.

6. TAKE A BALANCED VIEW OF THE GREAT BAKED BEAN CONTROVERSY

All your life, you've heard experts arguing about *big* issues, like the environment and the economy. Now, *add* to that list The Great Baked Bean Controversy. In case the excitement has passed you by, the question is: should baked beans be recommended to those on weight-loss diets? There's some medical evidence to support the idea that beans help to reduce high levels of blood cholesterol. It seems an unlikely idea, but – as doctors say – 'there it is'. Here's how the controversy breaks down:

The Good News

Baked beans may help to control blood cholesterol levels. They are known to be high in fibre, and *low in fats*. Best of all . . . they're already cooked.

The Bad News

Because of the way popular brands of tinned baked beans are processed and prepared, they tend to be *high in calories*. For example: one 8 ounce (220g) tin contains approximately 160 calories. A tin of so-called 'diet' baked beans isn't much better at 122 calories per tin. If you are dieting to lose weight, this may amount to between one-eighth and one-tenth of your total daily calorie allowance.

Conclusion:

Eat baked beans sparingly. In any case some claim that large quantities cause flatulence. It's bad enough to be hungry while dieting. Who wants to be socially unacceptable?

7. RUTHLESSLY ELIMINATE FAT
(THE F-WORD)

FAT. It's what you've got too much of, and wish to shed. It, on the other hand, has different ideas. It feels right at home on your hips, and wants to stick around. As every dieter knows, it is easier to move a mountain with a shovel than to dislodge the average fat cell. *Female* fat cells, it appears, are particularly stubborn. Put an ear to a well-padded thigh, and you can virtually hear them humming, 'We shall not be moved.'

There is, it seems, only one effective course of action. You have to *starve* them out. The idea is to deprive them of new (incoming) company until, weakened by loneliness, they become depressed and lose the will to live.

Here's How

Get tough, and eliminate from your daily diet most *saturated* (animal or dairy) fats. These fats, doctors tell us, increase blood cholesterol levels, and encourage the formation of body fat. They can clog arteries in the process, leading to heart disease. Who needs it? No lamb chop is worth the aggro.

Furthermore (ask any dieter), something in a fatty's metabolic make-up seems programmed to 'bond' with fat. *Any* passing fat. Fast, starve, subsist for days on a few raw vegetables and a packet of (salt free) rice cakes, and maddeningly, frustratingly, *nothing happens*. Your scale stays firmly fixed. Then, eat one Walnut Whip and it's Fat City. Up 5 pounds.

In short, the odds are stacked against you, and it isn't fair. This means that fatties must be utterly determined and single-minded in order to effectively fight flab. Winning the war means attacking on several fronts at once: nutritional, psychological and behavioural. For instance:

Here are Three Words That Should Never Again Cross Your Lips

(Don't say them. Don't even think about them. Certainly don't *eat* them):

1. suet
2. lard
3. dripping.

You don't need them. Never have. Never will. You can live the rest of your life very nicely without them.

Saturated fats are found not only in the above unmentionables – but also in meat: beef, lamb, pork, sausages and processed meats. They're present in the skin of poultry (dieters should take care to remove skin from chicken and turkey, preferably *before* cooking). Dairy products – milk, cheese, butter and egg yolks – contain saturated fats, as do baked goods (i.e. cakes, biscuits, pastries and puddings). Just to confuse the issue, saturated or 'bad' fats are present in some vegetable oils, but not others. Peanut oil is to be avoided, as are coconut and palm oils. Instead, dieters should choose sesame, sunflower, walnut, soya and certain varieties of olive oil – and in very small quantities.

No prizes for guessing that 'bad' fats are found in all the things you *love*: chocolates, crisps, sauces, hard margarines and ice cream. Even digestive biscuits and innocuous cream crackers often contain this nutritional time bomb. Cheap shot! It is easy to be fooled by the notion that, if you're eating anything as mind-numbingly dull as a cream cracker, it can't be doing much harm.

All this poses a great (unanswered) philosophical question: IF THE GODS DON'T WANT US TO EAT ICE CREAM, WHY MAKE IT *TASTE* SO GOOD? This has baffled the best minds of our time, and would no doubt have perplexed Socrates, had he come across Häagen-Dazs. (Plato's *Republic* might have been retitled *Fudge Ripple*.)

Anyway, according to medical experts, we can all live very nicely with *no* intake of saturated fats. You will probably choose to eat some foods which contain them – lean beef, for example – but do not imagine that even small amounts of the fats themselves are necessary to health.

The Right Stuff

On the other hand, our bodies do need small amounts of *polyunsaturated* fats in order to produce and repair body cells. Polyunsaturates are commonly found in selected vegetable oils (see above) and 'soft' margarines ... but read labels carefully, and ask questions if in doubt. Be equally careful with nuts, which are nutritional traitors. Many are high in polyunsaturates – but also in calories. Oily fish – such as herring, mackerel and trout – contain polyunsaturates, and are now thought to help protect the body against heart disease. Grill, steam or bake – do *not* fry them in a polyunsaturated spread.

THIN-THINK

The message is: cut down on the *total* amount of fat you eat, and avoid saturated fats. Poly-unsaturated spreads and oils should be used very sparingly, if at all. A scrape of Flora is preferable to a dollop of dripping, but still contains fats and calories. Dieters should eat plenty of fish of all sorts, but these should be cooked without adding fat (instead, try a dash of white wine or lemon juice, or a sprinkling of fresh dill and paprika). You'll feel like a gourmet cook without straining your stretch Lycra.

REMEMBER

Polyunsaturated foods don't contain *less* fat, just a *different kind* of fat, which the body metabolizes differently. **They can still be high in calories.**

That's pretty much all the science required in order to diet effectively. Once you've taken on board the idea that there are fats and *fats*, you're ready for action. Armed with information about *what* to eat (very little), your next task is to work out personal strategies for coping with restriction. Does a weight-loss or weight-maintenance programme *have* to be boring? *You bet!* Here are a few tips which may help:

Nine 'THIN-THINK' Tips
A Rough Guide to Success

1. YOG-THINK

Very low fat plain yogurt is a good friend to have around. Read labels carefully to make sure that it is indeed *very* low fat. Loseley's brand, for example, is excellent. Your yogurt should deliver around 60 calories per small (5oz, 140g) container. Some 'low fat' varieties contain nearly twice that number.

Try a tablespoonful in a jacket potato, and add a sprinkling of chives. Or, mash boiled potatoes with yogurt instead of butter, and season with a twist of fresh black pepper.

Better still: eat the yogurt as a snack. Again, a small container will set you back only 60 to 80 calories. By contrast, an equal amount of *anything flavoured* – even if it calls itself 'diet' or 'low fat' yogurt – will probably contain double the calories. For a bit of interest, sprinkle your plain yogurt with a touch of cinnamon . . . or mix in a dash of vanilla or coffee essence, half a sliced banana or a few fresh strawberries. Not necessarily together.

2. ALL COTTAGE CHEESE IS NOT EQUAL

Long perceived as a 'diet' food, cottage cheese can fool you. Some brands are creamy, salty, and high enough in calories (if not fats) to defeat the whole purpose of eating something so dull in the first place. The *smallest* supermarket container (4 oz, 110g) of plain, natural cottage cheese contains nearly 100 calories – which may account for 10 per cent of permitted daily intake.

Dieters who mean business should choose the dryer, relatively salt-free skimmed milk varieties. Again, compare calorie-counts carefully, and 'shop around' for the lowest. This can be difficult, since nutritional information on most packaging can be read only with the aid of the Hubble telescope. The best test is: if you are *enjoying* the cottage cheese, it is probably fattening and undermining your hard work. The serious low-fat kind looks and tastes pretty much like styrofoam packing material. Anything that awful *has* to be effective.

3. HOLD THE CHEESE

With a few honourable exceptions (fromage frais and various goat cheeses) most cheeses are relatively high in saturated fats. OK, some are lower than others (Camembert, Feta, Ricotta) but the relationship is much the same as butter to margarine. In other words: *you're better off without it* while you're trying to lose weight. This also goes (unfortunately) for the mountains of mouth-watering grated Parmesan you dump on your minestrone soup or pasta.

> ### *FAT-THINK*
>
> **Pasta's not fattening. But I can't eat it unless it *tastes* good. A little grated Parmesan is only a few extra calories.**

> ### *THIN-THINK*
>
> **Skip the cheese. I want to be thinner *now*. Who needs stuff which slows me down?**

4. RUTHLESS PRUNING

Wherever possible, while dieting, eliminate *unimportant* calories: the Parmesan on your pasta, the sugar in your coffee, the second glass of wine with dinner. It's surprising what a difference this can make. Ruthless 'pruning' is specially helpful if your weight appears to stick at one level. Half a teaspoon of sugar in coffee may not seem much . . . but drink five cups a day, and it soon adds up, stalling your progress. Review your diet regularly in search of spare calories.

When you're a natural fatty, fighting your own metabolism, you have to play hardball. Even one glass of wine a day may give fat cells the incentive they need to stick around. So, get tough with 'empty' or marginal calories. You won't feel *fuller* because you've had sugar in tea or grated cheese on spaghetti. When you diet, every morsel you eat has a job to do . . . to forestall hunger without adding fat. If your calories aren't working for you – cut them out.

5. STICK WITH CHICKEN

Chicken, fish and turkey are about as diet-friendly as food gets. For aspiring skinnies, the cooking method is important (grill, poach, boil, steam or roast). When dealing with poultry, it's absolutely vital to *remove the skin*. Yes, the crisp skin of a well-roasted chicken tastes great. This is your first clue that you shouldn't be eating it. It is 100 per cent pure fat, and you know what *that* does. Once in your system, it forms a molecular bond with existing flab.

And Now . . . Prepare to be Shocked

Many experts recommend eating more chicken and fish – and less red meat – for effective weight loss. Some doctors go on to advise that dieters should limit themselves to only 3 to 4 ounces of 'animal protein' (poultry, meat or fish) per day.

Now, here's the corker: do you know how *small* 3 to 4 ounces is?? No – *not* the size of the average supermarket portion of chicken breast. *Much* smaller. *Not* the size of the average pre-packed fillet of lemon sole, either. *Much* smaller.

For your guidance, here is a life-sized (scale) drawing of a 3 to 4 ounce serving of cooked chicken as it should appear on your plate. Overhead view, followed by side elevations, or profile:

3–4 oz helping of chicken breast

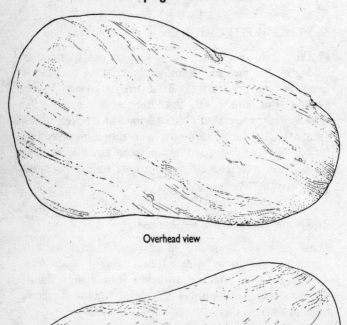

Overhead view

Side view

| 0 | 10 | 20 | 30 | 40 | 50 | 60 | 70 | 80 | 90 |

Depressing, right? You could call it the Story of Chicken Little. Furthermore, a 3 to 4 ounce serving of fish is not much bigger. Take, for example, fresh salmon; poached, as recommended, and garnished with a few exciting pink peppercorns. (Your threshold of excitement gets pretty low when dieting):

3– 4 oz helping of poached salmon

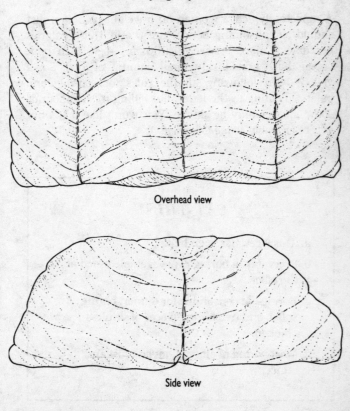

Overhead view

Side view

0   10   20   30   40   50   60   70   80   90

You now know the hideous truth. If you *really* want to lose weight, you can't actually eat much of *anything*. Your 3 to 4 ounces of 'animal protein' (the very phrase is enough to spoil your appetite) can be consumed at either lunch or dinner. Oh, the thrill of it all! It follows, if you think about it, that the remaining meals must be composed largely of vegetables, fruits, pulses, low-fat dairy products and carbohydrates.

A moderately active woman on a weight-reduction diet should be consuming between 800 and 1,200 calories per day; a man, between 1,000 and 1,500. In both cases, that's a relatively small amount of food. So, if you've been following all the rules for sensible and balanced eating to the letter, but failing to shed pounds – the answer may be simple. You won't like it . . . but you're probably *eating too much*.

FAT-THINK

a. This week has been hell.

b. Every day, a boring raw vegetable lunch at the office.

c. Boring old consommé for dinner, boring salad, and two boring pieces of skinless chicken.

d. Most boring of all . . . I haven't lost an ounce!

THIN-THINK

a. OK. This is war.

b. Let's cut the chicken ration to *one* small piece.

c. Add a fresh apple or some plain very low fat yogurt to stave off hunger.

d. *Walk* up the five flights to my office.

e. Fat cells, say your prayers.

6. SUGAR TAKES ITS LUMPS

Poor old sugar. For years, it drew all the fire; targeted as the biggest nutritional 'no no' while experts virtually ignored the harmful effect of fats. 'Pure, white, and deadly', they called it. A source of 'empty' calories with no other nutrients ... no vitamins, minerals, fibre or protein. What's more, it attacks tooth enamel and causes cavities. Aw, heck.

No wonder Brits hang their heads in shame when re-minded that they consume more sugar per capita than *any other nation* in the world. Even the well-padded Austrian matrons seen in Viennese tearooms spooning in *Sachertorte mit schlag* have nothing on Brits. We consume a one-pound bag of sugar per person, per week! (Goodness knows what we're doing with it – but some people must have trouble *lifting* a cup of tea.) Worse, we get through a *second* pound per person when you count the sugar added to processed foods such as sweets, soft drinks, biscuits and cakes. It probably takes a one-pound bag to ice the traditional British birthday cake ... not so much *frosted* as *preserved* in a sugar shell thick enough to prevent nuclear meltdown. Britain, it seems, is a nation on a permanent sugar 'high'.

Of course, every serious dieter should try to cut sugar consumption to a minimum. But, the trick is to do the same thing with *fats* – which are less well understood, and even more subversive because they are harder to spot. For example:

FAT-THINK AT BREAKFAST

a. No sugar in my coffee, thanks. I'll take some artificial sweetener.

b. Don't butter the toast. Just pass the Flora.

THIN-THINK AT BREAKFAST

a. Splash of skimmed milk in the coffee, please. No sugar.

b. Bowl of oat bran, skimmed milk – and half a sliced banana on top.

FAT-THINK AT LUNCH-TIME

a. Egg mayonnaise sandwich, please . . . and a Diet Coke.

THIN-THINK AT LUNCH-TIME

a. Sliced turkey on wholemeal with lettuce and tomato, please. No butter on the bread!

FAT-THINK AT DINNER-TIME

a. I'll give the chocolate gateau a miss. How's about fresh fruit salad – and a bit of that nice cheddar?

THIN-THINK AT DINNER-TIME

a. How's about fresh fruit salad?

The point is that fatties should beware of targeting the wrong culprit – or picking off only one out of two.

You should also be alert to sugar's 'hidden' disadvantage. This may sound harsh, but adding it to food encourages you to *enjoy* eating too much. You're more likely to keep going long after your tum has registered 'full' because of the pure pleasure of a sweet taste. How many people are still hungry by the time they tuck into dessert?

Because sweet foods are low in fibre, they're not filling. That's why it's so easy to put away a traditional Sunday lunch, and still find room for the trifle.

Just to throw you off the track, sugar comes in many forms. Conscientious readers of labels should be on the lookout for: sucrose, glucose, dextrose, fructose and maltose. All of them are fattening. (For the avoidance of doubt, 'raw' or brown sugar is no less fattening than processed white.) Sugar is sugar. Moreover, sugar is *sneaky*. It hides in unexpected places, like crisps and tinned soup. It's a main component of many breakfast cereals – even ones which aren't obviously 'frosted' with tiny white granules. Some brands of 'healthy' muesli, for example, are very high in sugar. So are 'natural' sweeteners, such as honey, syrup and molasses. Ageing beauty queens may swear that honey provides energy, is the nectar of the queen bee, and contains the secret of eternal youth . . . but it also makes you *fat*.

FAT-THINK

a. I'm on a painless diet.

b. I rely on diet colas. Only 1 calorie per can!

c. Most days, I knock back a six-pack.

d. I buy a special weight-watchers' strawberry mousse made with NutraSweet.

e. I take pills to suppress my appetite.

f. And I put artificial sweeteners in tea and coffee.

g. Then I remember my contraceptive pill and a Multi-Vite.

h. I've never felt worse in my life.

Magic Bullet

There are probably more people out there looking for a magic weight-loss 'bullet' than for the origins of the universe. (*Finding it* would no doubt be more profitable.) Everyone wants a 'painless' way to lose weight. We all want to continue eating the foods we enjoy, while at the same time shedding spare pounds. No wonder many regard artificial sweeteners as the perfect solution. On paper, it looks great. A whole can of Diet Coke sets you back only 1 calorie! So, what's the *bad* news? (How long have you got?)

Get ready . . . here it comes

a. *Artificial sweeteners are chemicals.* There is evidence that heavy reliance on them can damage health. Some, for example, work on your kidneys, causing frequent urination. You're better off with a few calories-worth of sugar in your tea, if you can't do without.

b. *Use of sugar substitutes may increase demand for the real thing.* When the body takes in natural sugar, the pancreas is stimulated to produce insulin, which – in a normal person – 'neutralizes' the sugar in the bloodstream. If not enough insulin is produced, a high sugar count – or diabetes – can result.

There is now evidence to suggest that excessive intake of artificial sweeteners *also* triggers the production of insulin. It apparently wanders around the system, looking (in vain) for something to neutralize. This, in turn, can cause you to crave *more* sweet or sugary foods in order to right the balance.

c. *People who maintain bad old habits with the aid of food substitutes are kidding themselves.* They sprinkle Canderel on their cornflakes. They swig Diet Fanta, eat 'cholesterol free' frozen yogurt, and drown their salads in creamy 'low fat' dressings. They spread diet cream cheese on toast, treat themselves to 'lite' beers, and say goodnight with a cup of no-cal cocoa. They are amazed (and aggrieved) when unwanted pounds fail to disappear.

Fatties' Fact File:

a. THERE ARE *NO SUCH THINGS* AS:

> painless childbirth
> painless dentistry
> painless career success
> painless 'relationships'

. . . and

b. THERE IS NO *PAINLESS* WAY TO LOSE WEIGHT
(AND KEEP IT OFF).

First: if you convince yourself that you can eat or drink
something with impunity because it is virtually
'calorie-free', you will tend to do so . . . whether or not
you are – strictly speaking – *hungry*. In order to make
weight-loss diets work (and, just as importantly, to
maintain your new weight) you must form the habit of
linking food intake *directly* to hunger. THIN-THINK
means relying on a balanced, low-fat diet, and learning
to stop eating as soon as you are full. Cans of Diet Coke
and no-cal indulgences cloud the issue, and blur the
lines.

Second: if the stuff tastes sweet and pleasant, you will
easily lose your perception of quantity, and eat or drink
more than you intended.

Third: unless you adopt sensible (and disciplined) eating
habits, you will never – repeat, *never* – maintain a slim
figure. Your job is to learn to cope with a restricted – yet
balanced – diet . . . to 'manage' hunger, and to resist the
compulsive urge to put things in your mouth even
when you're not hungry. None of this can be accomplished by relying on phoney food. Those who use it to
'fill the gap' and make dieting painless can expect disappointment.

So, scrap those daily cans of soft drink in favour of fizzy
mineral water, sugarless tea or coffee. Freshly squeezed
fruit juices (no sugar added) are also good, though these
can be higher in calories than you may expect. Try

diluting them with fizzy mineral water. *Or*, drink *plain water*! Six medium-sized glasses a day are generally recommended on any weight-loss diet.

Don't – for heaven's sake – make a habit of eating 'diet' chocolate bars, salad creams, sauces or ice creams. As has been said before, you won't be able to do that in real life. Furthermore, careful inspection soon reveals that many products labelled 'diet' or 'low fat' are still relatively high in calories. The conclusion is clear: to achieve your ideal figure, *you've* got to do the hard work. No passing the buck to the makers of NutraSweet.

7. PINCH OF SALT

Much the same is true of *salt* substitutes. Dieters are usually advised to cut down on salt for two reasons:

a. In some people, too high a salt intake raises blood pressure.

b. Salt encourages body tissues to retain water – the *last* thing you want when attempting to slim.

As with sugar, adding salt to food somehow seduces you into eating more than you'd intended. In certain cases (where, for example, high blood pressure is present) salt substitutes may be deemed preferable to the real thing. Most, however, still contain some salt . . . and don't help you to change habits.

Everyone needs *some* salt (about 1g a day) but, in Britain, most people take in around 10. Approximately half of it is hiding in processed food (for example: tinned soup, bread . . . and even your old friend, cottage cheese). The rest is added in cooking or at the table – and a bit is naturally present in foods. If you're eating a balanced diet, you'll be getting plenty of salt without having to add more. Don't fall for the old 'sea salt is good for you' line. Sea salt does contain some minerals – but otherwise has the same disadvantages as ordinary stuff. Salting food can also be rather habit-forming. Watch overweight people in restaurants, and you'll see that many literally *pour* salt on food – as a kind of ritual – before even tasting it.

8. SNACKS, LIES AND FORMULA DIETS

It's been said many times, but is worth repeating: manufacturers' 'formula diets' are at odds with the principles of THIN-THINK, and are not helpful to dieters as part of a long-term strategy for staying slim. It's phoney food time again . . . as fatties are encouraged to replace a meal or two with specially formulated drinks or bars. There are too many 'meal replacements' on the market to mention, but favourites include: the Cambridge Diet, Slim-Fast, and – Oprah Winfrey's alleged personal choice – Optifast.

It is easy to see why such 'magic potions' are attractive to slimmers. First, because they keep calorie intake so low (600 to 900 calories per day is typical) they can produce quick results before dieters become discouraged. Second, they are idiot-proof. By providing your entire intake in one convenient package, they eliminate possibilities of error or temptation. There are no difficult calorie-counts to work out, no juggling with portion control or nutritional balance. You've got it – so to speak – on a plate. Just follow the instructions and, hey, presto – you're a sylph.

What's wrong, then? Many things. Some brand diets are considered unsafe – even life-threatening – with calorie-counts far too low to be followed for extended periods. Some contain chemicals or artificial proteins which can damage health. Some lack the ingredients for proper nutritional balance, and 'starve' the body of essential requirements.

But, even high-quality, well-formulated products of this nature have a major drawback. They *do not* retrain mind and body, or allow you to develop appropriate new eating habits which will serve you well in the future. The vast majority of formula plan dieters regain all weight lost – and then some – as soon as they resume 'normal' eating. The promised 'quick fix' becomes a long-term liability. (See Oprah Winfrey, stones heavier after her formula 'fast'.) Many people imagine that they can 'kick-start' their diets with meal replacements, then wean themselves gradually onto 'proper' diet food. Research shows that this strategy is unlikely to succeed. Lesson: there are no short-cuts, no magic potions, no undiscovered secrets. To successfully lose weight and keep it off, you have to learn to deal with *real* food in *real* life. And you have to do it yourself. So, bite the bullet. (At least it's not fattening.)

9. THE IMPORTANCE OF SUFFERING

Finally, there is another reason to avoid fake food designed to make dieting painless. My theory – developed after years of deep thinking in the bathtub – is that successful weight loss and *suffering* are bio-chemically linked. Inextricably, and endocrinologically. Do not allow your body to catch you *enjoying* food. There's something about enjoyment which seems to undermine diets.

Maybe it's simply because – without noticing – we tend to eat more of foods we enjoy. Or, perhaps body chemistry moves in mysterious ways, and the impact of 'pleasure' is poorly understood. Whatever the reason, one thing is sure: show your body *too good a time* while dieting ('I'll use my calorie allowance on one ice cream cone, and won't eat another thing all day!') and you won't lose an ounce. Fat cells will simply hang around, hoping for more fun. If you want to get rid of them, it's best to bore them with bran, flush them out with monotonous fibre. This has the same effect on *them* as it does on *you*. It makes them lose the will to live. (Sobbing aloud while eating delivers a clear signal, and probably helps.)

6
THE CALORIE CON

There are more diet books on the market than fatties have had Egg McMuffins. Chances are that you've flirted with F-Plan, Hip and Thigh, Rotation, Scarsdale, Pineapple, Beverly Hills . . . and everything along the lines of Eat-All-You-Want-and-Lose-Weight. Chances are that you're still pounds heavier than you want to be.

It's remarkable that books often fail to address what is – for most fatties – the *key* issue: how to cope with self-denial, and feelings of powerlessness over food. Instead, they propose 'simple formulae' for weight loss. They say that if we limit ourselves to 1,000 calories a day, we'll be *thin*. So much protein, so much calcium, so much complex carbohydrate, and pounds will melt away. We have only to follow the rules, not forgetting particular rituals. (These vary according to the book, but may involve 6 ounces of fresh pineapple or eight large glasses of water or thirty minutes of aerobic workout a day.) Some recommend 'combination' eating: certain foods in certain combinations, in a certain order, in certain amounts, at certain times of the day. Dutifully, we live on mangos and eliminate beetroot. In no time at all, they promise, we'll look like Jane, or Rosemary. Or Cindy, or Cher. Or a Chippendale. Or the unidentified (but enviable) creature on the cover, turned sideways to display a flat tum.

If only weight loss were as simple as a mere calorie count would suggest! Few of these works, however, contain hints on how to develop the cast-iron will-power required to follow *any* plan; to reduce weight and keep it off. They don't mention hunger. They don't mention temptation, let alone compulsion. They don't mention Cadbury's.

The fact is that most fatties cannot gain control of eating habits simply by following a nutritional blueprint. They first need to tackle a fundamental 'attitude' problem; how to accept – and then live with – long-term, self-inflicted food restriction. Master that, and the issue of exactly *what* you eat is a mere detail.

EATING BY NUMBERS

Even for those with great will-power, calorie-counting can be misleading – and ultimately defeating. Doctors suggest 'magic numbers' to be achieved, based on average metabolic rates. For example: the average (moderately active) man burns around 2,600 calories per day, the average woman 2,000. It follows that a calorie intake of about 1,500 for men and 1,200 for women should soon result in weight loss. *Should*. But this ignores certain important variables:

1. Many people with weight problems have metabolic rates which are lower (or more sluggish) than average. Rates can be further depressed by years of 'Yo-Yo' dieting (repeated weight loss and gain). Such people

may find it increasingly difficult to lose weight, even on severely reduced numbers of calories. If in doubt, your 'resting' metabolic rate can be measured by a doctor, who will simply ask you to relax for twenty minutes, and breathe into a special measuring mask.

Should your rate prove low or sluggish, there are three courses of action available:

a. You can exercise regularly and vigorously, which is known to raise metabolic rate and burn more calories.

b. You can restrict your calorie intake still further by eating even less.

c. Or both.

2. Metabolic rate is not a 'constant'. It changes throughout life. (Usually when you're not looking.)

For example: most people find that they seem to burn calories more efficiently in youth than middle age, when metabolic rate progressively slows. The very elderly can get by – indeed, often appear to thrive – on quite small amounts of food, as their appetites decrease in line with diminished energy requirements. However, many in (or at the brink of) middle age experience problems. Slowly, imperceptibly – weight creeps up. Waistbands get snug; suits look outgrown. The man who – at twenty-two – routinely scoffed two burgers and double fries at a sitting while his stomach stayed flat as a board, notices that he's beginning to develop a 'paunch'. A woman exchanges her slender young shape for a more rounded and 'matronly' figure (which she may ascribe to childbirth).

The bottom line is that they cannot eat as they once did without piling on pounds. The very idea is hard to accept, and requires a period of adjustment. You may argue that you're 'just as active' in your late thirties as you were in your mid-twenties. (True – you admit – your old clothes are *smaller* – but that's a result of inferior dry-cleaning.)

When you get past what psychologists refer to as the 'denial' stage, you get *angry*. Life, you realize, is a real swizz. Habits which served you well early in life must now be broken. In order to maintain an attractive shape, you will have to forgo pleasures, eat less, and exercise more. You must be prepared to constantly adapt behaviour to ever-decreasing calorie requirements. (To add insult to injury, you're probably *working* harder than you ever did in your twenties.) A woman who, at twenty-five, easily shed pounds on a daily intake of 1,200 calories may, at thirty-eight, be forced to cut back to 1,000. Frankly, that's not much food.

3. Metabolic rate – particularly in females – can vary slightly from week to week. Many women report, for example, that they are specially hungry in the week before a menstrual period. Latest medical research indicates that calorie requirements do indeed increase slightly at that time . . . though the reasons are unclear. During pregnancy, women are naturally inclined to eat more to sustain a developing baby. The same is true while they are breast-feeding.

The more acute hunger felt at the onset of a period is a bit of a problem. It is tempting to conclude that women should allow themselves more food at this time because it is 'natural' to want to eat. But, we're into dangerous territory! Extra food consumed pre-period is, unhappily, just as fattening as at other times of the month. There is no real evidence that the process of menstruation 'burns' additional calories or that these are somehow magically shed at the end of the cycle. Increased intake may contribute to the 'bloating' which many feel. Pounds gained may prove difficult to dislodge when the period is over. Then – before you know it – you're *ravenous* . . . and eating more again in preparation for the *next* period. This, no doubt, is what is meant by 'vicious cycle'.

It's better, perhaps, to resist the 'feeding instinct' where possible – or strive to satisfy it with carrot sticks and a raw apple instead of the 2 pound box of Black Magic you naturally crave. Lesson: those who truly wish to be thin should not assume that nature is on their side.

4. Most experts agree that physical exercise burns calories. Regular activity can raise metabolic rate, which allows you to eat a bit more without storing excess

calories in the form of body fat. But, here, too, a balance must be struck. We all know that vigorous workouts can stimulate appetite. Unless you satisfy resulting hunger with foods low in sugar and fat, you won't benefit. No point in jogging ten miles, swimming forty laps, then stoking up like Geoff Capes or Fatima Whitbread. *Fit* is not the same thing as *slim*. If you're in any doubt, look at the average Sumo wrestler.

5. 'Yo-Yo' diets. Many habitual dieters lose and regain weight time after wearying time. They go up and down more often than Otis elevators. If at first they don't succeed, they try, try again. Endocrinologically speaking, their lives represent a triumph of hope over experience.

In the late eighties, a study at the University of Pennsylvania observed that some women attending the medical school's obesity clinic failed to lose weight on an intake of only 800 to 900 calories a day. Further investigation revealed that they were the patients whose weight had fluctuated most over a period of years. In short, *they'd been on the most diets.*

New research indicates that 'Yo-Yo' dieting increases the activity of an annoying little enzyme called lipoprotein lipase, which promotes the storage of body fat. The result is that weight loss becomes more and more difficult – even on 'starvation' rations. It seems that our bodies are programmed to conserve calories. Back in the mists of time, this mechanism no doubt helped to preserve the species in times of food scarcity. (It's safe to say that cave dwellers were probably more concerned with staying alive than looking great in Azzedine Alaïa.)

Today, so the theory goes – this genetic 'regulator' is maladaptive. That's to say that it inhibits your ability to control your own weight at a time when food supplies are constantly available. (All it takes is a 'phone call to Pizza Hut.) Some doctors therefore advise that you should begin a diet only when your motivation is high, and you're determined to *succeed*.

It's probably best, they argue, to get it right the first time. If in doubt . . . *wait*.

AVOIDING CONFUSION

One of the most unsettling things about dieting is the amount of *conflicting advice* which would-be skinnies receive. The subject is fraught with uncertainty and divided opinion. Much of what is said and written (and that's a lot!) is at best speculation – and at worst, voodoo.

DIETING MAKES YOU FAT! shrieks a headline. The article goes on to explain that prolonged slimming slows your metabolic rate, and makes it harder to shed pounds without sustained exercise. Some truth here, of course, but the conclusion is unjustified. Every slimmer experiences the frustration of metabolic slow-down – and suffers the food-obsession that goes with it. But it does not follow that we shouldn't *try* to lose weight . . . or that dieting 'makes you fat'. Nor can we assume that *not* dieting will succeed in making us slim.

There have been whole books explaining that *Fat Is a*

Feminist Issue, and countless magazine features on how to 'Stop Dieting and Lose Weight' (conquer your food fixation, and magically shed pounds). And finally – solace for long-term recidivist fatties – 'Size 16 and Beautiful – Coming to Terms With Your Weight'. Cop out. It's like writing an article called 'How to Stop Worrying and Love the Bomb.'

Having resolved the issue of *whether or not* to diet, a wannabe skinny must decide *which* programme to follow. The choice is mind-boggling. You can simply cut calories and exercise . . . or eat from certain food groups according to a 'plan'. No eggs, decrees one authority. Never combine proteins with complex carbohydrates, warns another. Eliminate gluten, but 'pig out' on gherkins.

The inescapable conclusion is that *diet* is one of the most controversial subjects in the world . . . right up there with The Meaning of Life and whether Madonna has real talent. It's also one of life's dark areas. Experts can't agree on it – so really, your guess is as good as mine. Or Jane's or Cher's.

We must, of course, rely on conventional medical wisdom about fats, proteins, carbohydrates and calories. But, for many Bunters and Bunterettes, these terms have no real meaning. How will certain categories of food behave in the body, individually or in combination? Will slavish devotion to the rules guarantee weight loss? Nnnnot really.

Scientists have been aware – for most of this century – of the connection between calories and obesity. Today, they are learning much about the effect of saturated fats on health. But, no one can yet explain the *variable* relationship between what a person eats – and how fat he or she becomes. Why can some lucky skinnies gorge on 'forbidden' foods and remain stick-thin, while others gain weight simply by sniffing a doughnut? How disappointing that, for centuries, great minds have consistently failed to shed light on life's most burning questions:

The Universe's Five Great Philosophical Questions

(**in *reverse* order of importance**):

     5. Why are we here?

     4. What is the meaning of life?

     3. Why do the good suffer?

     2. Why do small eaters gain weight? (And why is it easier to gain a pound than to lose one?)

     1. IF GOD WANTS US TO EAT LETTUCE, WHY DID HE INVENT HÄAGEN-DAZS?

                                      . . . now read on.

7

RECOLLECTIONS OF A FAT KID

Oh, how I hated skinny kids! The ones who had to be patiently coaxed to swallow a few life-sustaining morsels. The ones who'd sniff their food with deep distrust before venturing to taste it, fearful of making tongue-contact with something nasty. Couldn't they just spit it out, I wondered, if strictly necessary?

Such wariness was baffling to me. A testy relationship with food was not my style. I rarely found it necessary to spit *anything* out – unless pieces of packaging got stuck in the apple sauce. The only thing I ever wanted to do with food was swallow it.

Skinny kids had tummies so flat that a ruler would rest on both hipbones without touching the navel. The girls' trim upper arms emerged prettily from sleeveless shirts or halter-neck tops. The fashionable 'African' bracelets worn above the elbow did not appear (as mine did) to be stopping the circulation. Most remarkable of all – none of their body-parts *chaffed*. They had thin legs with plenty of space in between, so that the inner thighs did not rub together as they walked. In fact, they did not seem to *have* thighs. (A skinny kid's leg is thickest around the knee). Their ribs showed, even with their arms down at their sides. Mine didn't. I was well-padded from earliest childhood. Looking back, it seems I started watching my weight at about the same time I gave up midnight feeds.

My playmates did not seem to *feel* hunger. They knew it was time to eat when their mothers called them, but did not crave food or enjoy it – except things like ice cream and crisps. They were given lots of those by craven adults who feared they'd otherwise waste away. Skinny kids regarded the whole process of taking nourishment as a nuisance – an unwelcome interruption to the serious business of childhood. At mealtimes, they delayed coming to the table, and begged to leave it as soon as possible, in order to return to boisterous play. Not me! No activity was as pleasant as finishing what was on my plate . . . and I was never diverted by other attractions while a single bite remained.

At the age of eleven or twelve, I was probably 15 to 20 pounds overweight. Sweet old ladies and sales assistants in department stores said I was 'pleasingly plump' – but I knew those were polite words for 'fat'. At school, every gym class was a trial, as I waited to be last chosen when team captains picked sides. Of course, I couldn't run as fast as skinny kids (slowed by the friction of my inner thighs). I longed to be able to scamper up ropes like the others, or move deftly by my arms along a climbing frame . . . but it was not to be. *Both* hands were required to support my weight. It was impossible to release one in order to swing from rung to rung.

Perhaps most painful of all was my secret crush on the cutest boy in the class. I adored him, but made a point of being aloof to protect myself from hope, and wounding rejection. I also avoided girlfriends who were too thin

and flirty, fearing comparison. I cultivated academic skills to make up for physical ones, and took part in activities only if they could be performed while sitting down. This left me a limited range which included Scrabble, tiddly winks and snacking.

WHO LOVES A FATTY?
(FATTIES AND SURVIVAL)

I learned early that, if you were prepared to make others laugh, and listen to their problems, you could make them like you even if you were fat. Thin girls' problems always involved *choices* . . . for example, which of two besotted boyfriends to choose. They felt safe confiding in a fat friend, consigned by size to the sidelines of life. By offering a service to skinnies, and counselling them on social lives you secretly envied, you could be part of the gang – and at least avoid being teased.

Even parents were a problem. In their anxiety to help you reduce, they could hardly avoid the suggestion that – although you were loved – you'd be extra lovable *thinner*.

Things Parents Say to Fat Kids

   a. You have such beautiful eyes/hair/skin. You'll be so *pretty* when you lose weight.

   b. The boys will be knocking the door down once you've lost weight.

   c. You have a lovely figure. You just need to lose weight.

   d. You'll like yourself *so much better* after you've lost weight!

My mother – sensitive to my feelings – was careful lest I be defeated by the scale of the problem. She was determined that I should see myself as 'a bit overweight' rather than *fat*. She skilfully protected me from the department store dragons who sell dresses to little girls. 'Too small around the waist, dear?' (Sorry shake of head.) 'I'm afraid it doesn't come larger. Perhaps you should try a "Chubby".'

Yes, back in the fifties and sixties, American marketing geniuses invented a range of outsized clothing for kids, and actually named them 'Chubbies'. Why not go the whole hog, I wondered, and call them 'Fatsos'? Or 'Slobettes'? Anyway, I would have attended school naked rather than be forced to wear them, and to see myself as a loathsome 'Chubby'. My mother – ever resourceful – simply found dresses which 'ran large', and let out every seam in order to preserve my dignity.

Adults did tend, however, to jump to conclusions about my eating habits. They assumed that I ate *too much* – and often took it upon themselves to impose restrictions. These were 'ad hoc', and had no reference to my wishes, or appetite.

This was infuriating, as well as hurtful. At family dinners, skinny cousins were helped to generous servings, because they needed 'building up'. When it came to me, there was strict portion control. Not only was I deprived, but – it seemed – somehow out-manoeuvred. Skinny kids, I soon saw, can *manipulate* adults with food. This is because it is a natural grown-up instinct to worry when a child won't eat. The picky little creep monopolizes their attention, as they coax and cajole, catering to each

whim and fancy. In desperation, they abandon any notion of balanced diet, and give in ... allowing skinny kids to eat as much as they like of anything they'll agree to put in their mouths.

If a fat kid did the same thing, he'd gain 6 pounds. The irony is that the skinny kid stays skinny. The adult is just grateful that he's alive.

I have vivid memories of bringing skinny friends home for lunch. My mother would put half a sandwich on my plate, accompanied by a glass of skimmed milk. She'd serve the friend a *whole* sandwich, plus the remaining half of mine ... and a glass of chocolate milk. For dessert, the friend got all the chocolate-covered marshmallow cookies she could eat, while I made do with an apple. To this day, I hate apples. At the end of lunch, I'd return to school hungry. 'She's always hungry,' they'd say. 'That's why she has a weight problem.'

One of the worst things about being a fat kid is that you are helpless; at the mercy of every adult (and there are many) who wishes to limit your intake. It is easy for grown-ups to impose constraints on you which they would not tolerate themselves. Somehow, you lose control of your own destiny. Skinny kids (who can out-run, out-play, and generally outlast you) are seen as weak, frail, and in need of care to preserve their tenuous grip on life. You – robust specimen – are something of an embarrassment. Perhaps it's 'fat kid paranoia' – but adults seem mildly disapproving – as if you'd secretly hoarded family resources, taking the lion's share of available nourishment. I used to imagine that they thought the skinny kids were skinny because I'd taken their *food*.

Adults who urge you to 'diet' (attain a size more acceptable to *them*) may have mixed motives. Some, who love you, no doubt wish to spare you the undeniable pain of being overweight: the teasing, the physical ineptitude, the loss of confidence. Others see in you a reflection of their own shortcomings, and dislike your body-shape as they do their own. They are quick to ration a child's portions . . . far slower to similarly restrict themselves.

Which brings me to the best, *best* thing about being a skinny kid. You enjoy the great luxury of being able to follow your inclinations, and do what comes *naturally*. You can eat when you're hungry – what you like, and as much as you wish. You can stop when you're full. Your lean and efficient body will obligingly 'self-regulate'. You need not distort natural patterns, revise needs, or second-guess requirements. You can eat without guilt. You can do what fatties never, ever manage: you can *forget about food*.

My theory is that, for most fatties, the highlight of life comes in infancy. It is 'demand' feeding ... our once-in-a-lifetime opportunity to link food with pure gratification. After that, things go (nutritionally speaking) downhill. Fat children soon learn that appetite must be censored and denied. Before long, eating becomes more of a problem than a pleasure. Furthermore, there's no improvement later in life, if statistics are to be believed. Remember that *most* adults are either on diets – or feel they ought to be. A large body of medical evidence supports the notion that fat kids become fat adults. The sole consolation is that lots of skinny kids *also* become real *porkers*.

Anyway, as I moved through childhood (with my tummy straining the zipper of my bermuda shorts) the *truth* dawned ...

The Truth

1. Life is *different* for slim people. Different and better.
2. It is better to be slim than even a few pounds overweight.

Having accepted the main proposition – and apart from any medical imperative – I could list countless and compelling reasons to become slim:

Reasons to Be Thinner – Part Two

1. Society's tolerance for the overweight or fat is limited. Unfair as it seems, people of slim or 'average' builds get more breaks than fatties.

2. Slim people can afford to be more discriminating in their choice of partners. Fatties are inclined to settle for what they can get.

3. Fat people are less likely to be judged on their merits. Fat *obscures* merit.

4. When you carry excess weight, others assume that you lack self-discipline, and that your life is 'out of control'.

5. This encourages them to offer unsolicited advice. (Being slim *discourages intrusion*.)

6. Evidence suggests that even talent and ability do not outweigh the significant disadvantage of being fat.

7. Unless you diet, you will never know what you *might* have achieved – socially and professionally – by being slim.

8. It is difficult to achieve real contentment in life when you are chronically dissatisfied with your weight.

9. It is far less painful to lose the weight than to spend years despising yourself for *not* losing it.

10. People who do not diet successfully waste precious years trying to reconcile their

ambitions to their body-size. It is preferable to
adapt body-size to ambitions.

The sheer inevitability of the need to diet dawned on me
early . . . but I took no real action until I was well into my
teens. At eighteen, I went away to university. My room-
mate, Marcia, was quick to point out that there are two
kinds of people in the world: the ones who hold a
conversation with you over dinner, and get so involved in
the subject, that they forget there's food on the fork . . . and
the ones who don't. We knew which category *I* fell into.

Matters reached a head as I entered my twenties. I'd
acquired a 'serious' boyfriend, considered myself a sophis-
ticate, and took to heart the popular adage that 'there's
no such thing as too skinny or too rich'. Like so many
young women (Princess Di, are you listening?) I decided
to be the former first, and the latter later. I went on a
rigorous – but balanced – diet. Low fat, low-cal, no
gimmicks. I was determined to be seriously, *fashionably*
thin. Changing my shape – and, as I saw it, my prospects
– had at last become more important to me than the
fleeting pleasure of dining-hall doughnuts, and Saturday
night quarter-pounders with cheese.

No, I didn't develop anorexia. (I didn't know it was
available.) But, I did lose weight – around 20 pounds of
it, bringing me to a nice, even $7\frac{1}{2}$ stone at 5'4". There
were no great secrets. I just cut down on everything, got
closely acquainted with fruits and vegetables, and entirely eliminated 'worst offenders': no ice cream, fried
foods or alcohol. You get the picture.

It took six to nine months, but I was sylph-like on my
wedding day. What I'd lost in cellulite, I'd gained in

iron-willed determination. I loathed dieting so much, that I decided never to be fat again. Not for me the soul-destroying life-long lurch up and down the bathroom scales. I would maintain my new figure – stay slim always. In other words, I so despised *strict* diets, that I resolved to follow a *modified* one forever.

And I have. (Apologies to those who expected a happier ending.) Yes, nutritionally speaking I am a paragon – with, I'm afraid, little patience for the infirm of purpose. I have now maintained a stable weight for eighteen years ... and feel in all honesty that the quality of life has improved, that it's better to be thin than even a few pounds overweight, and that – unfair as it seems – thin people get more breaks than fat ones.

But – and here's the irony of the situation – I'll always be a fat kid *psychologically*. My shape may have changed, but my self-image remains the same. When I gaze into the mirror, a twelve-year-old stares back – her tummy straining at the zipper of her bermuda shorts. At moments of anxiety – or if, for any reason, self-confidence slips – I automatically *feel* fat. Any perceived personal inadequacy, shortcoming or failure triggers this 'fat' reflex. 'No wonder I lost the contract,' I wail inwardly. 'Who'd give it to a *chub*?' (The competing merits of others seem irrelevant.)

All this serves as a reminder that weight may change, but self-image is slow to follow. Once a fatty, *always* (in some ways) a fatty.

THE GOOD NEWS

No doubt the reverse is true, too. Once a skinny, etc. Which brings me to the one piece of *good news* about being a fat kid. Your early folk-memory of yourself is the best insurance against regaining the lost weight. From earliest childhood, you appreciate the need for self-control and restraint. You learn to fight your own metabolism, and – very often – to win.

Not so, the favoured skinny kids of yore. Accustomed as they are to doing exactly what comes naturally, the changes of adulthood and the lessons of self-denial come hard. (For them, too, metabolic needs evolve with age, but youthful behaviour is often for keeps.) The bag-of-bones who – aged nine – downed crisps and sweets with no marked effect expects to do the same at thirty-five. Fat chance.

In short, former fat kids are often better at being slim adults. They have already notched up years of valuable practice. Once they've reached a target weight, they are ever alert to the presence of personal demons – aware that, inside every trim (but formerly fat) frame, there's an 18 stone person trying to get out.

NATURE, NURTURE AND NOURISHMENT

There is much fascinating research, these days, on the 'genetic' basis of overweight and obesity. Where – scientists are asking – do fat children come from? Very often, it seems, they are the product of fat parents ... but the nature vs. nurture question remains unresolved. Do junior chubs and chub-ettes somehow *inherit* a propensity to store fat – or do they gain weight simply because they follow the poor eating habits of their parents?

Experts speculate that some obese children may inherit an abnormally high number of fat cells ... or abnormally large cells. In addition, it is possible that they are genetically 'programmed' to have a slow metabolic rate. Another theory is that such children have an inborn tendency to move around or exercise *less* than other children – and hence burn fewer calories.

What is certain – according to latest British and American research – is that the size of all children consistently reflects the size of natural parents. One long term British project observed a group of obese mothers-to-be, and found that half of their children were clinically overweight by the time they were a year old. In another study carried out at the University of Pennsylvania Medical School, doctors concluded that '80 per cent of the children of obese parents become obese'.

If, at this point, you're blaming a fondness for cream cakes on your poor old parents – think again. Grow up! The same doctors stress that proper diet and exercise can successfully neutralize an inherited tendency. *Genes*, they emphasize, *are not destiny*.

It is certainly true, however, that being a formerly fat or skinny kid has a profound effect on self-image. In many ways, your early metabolic history 'programmes' you for life. This book is about *reprogramming* yourself . . . and – if necessary – flying in the face of genetic destiny. It helps, therefore, to identify your own starting-point. On which side of the (nutritional) blanket were *you* born? Here's a rough guide:

JUNIOR FAT-THINK, JUNIOR THIN-THINK

SKINNY KIDS . . .

open the freezer at the local newsagent's, and select the orange ice lolly because they honestly like it best.

FAT KIDS...

choose the Wall's Cornetto every time.

SKINNY KIDS...

won't eat food if it's greasy.

FAT KIDS...

enjoy the grease. It doubles as gravy.

SKINNY KIDS...

love summer. They look cool and comfortable in summer clothes, and continue to run and play when the weather's hot.

FAT KIDS...

don't. They slow down as the temperature rises. Their faces perspire, clothing looks tight, and fabric forms 'balls' where their thighs rub together. They get prickly heat rash between the tyres of fat around their midriffs.

SKINNY KIDS...

forget about the food on their plates when engaged in conversation. They would rather talk than eat.

FAT KIDS...

eat silently (except for the occasional 'grunt' of enjoyment).

SKINNY KIDS...

Eat on the run. They happily keep moving – or playing – even with an ice-cream cone in one hand.

FAT KIDS...

Sit *still* while eating. Food deserves undivided attention.

SKINNY KIDS...

are fussy about the presentation of food. Spaghetti loops must make a face on a slice of toast. Soup must appear in a favourite bowl. Fish fingers should 'line up' on the plate.

FAT KIDS...

will eat no matter how it looks. (If it's *food*, who cares about configuration?)

SKINNY KIDS...

are deeply suspicious of 'new' food. They will agree to eat only familiar food that they know and trust. The 'approved' list is short ... but includes orange squash, baked beans, Smarties and crisps.

FAT KIDS...

adore old favourites, but welcome the new – however exotic. (Bring on the lobster thermidor!) In general, they will eat anything that doesn't eat them first.

SKINNY KIDS...

lose their appetites when they feel a weeny bit off-colour.

FAT KIDS...

stop eating only when unconscious.

SKINNY KIDS...

do not feel 'urgent' hunger as acutely as fat kids. Often, they fail to register 'hunger' until they fall over. Furthermore, their small appetites are easily satisfied. (One Smartie takes the edge off.)

FAT KIDS...

get ravenous! Their hunger has a momentum of its own. They do not notice little signals from their tummies to their brains, which say:

> 'Starting to feel better, now . . .'

> 'getting full . . .'

> 'full.'

In fact, they register nothing short of

> 'STUFFED.'

Even then, there's room for dessert.

THIN-THINK KID

FAT-THINK KID

In short, food is such a pleasure for fat kids, that – unless, for some reason, it is physically impossible to go on eating – they do not stop. They don't understand why anyone *ever* stops. Still less do they comprehend why skinny kids never *start*.

8

FAT AND MOTHERS

*'Eat, Eat, It'll Do You Good!' (And Other Things
Your Mother Should Never Have Told You.)*

When it comes to fat (yours), mothers experience inner
turmoil. They have ambitions to make you the best
person you can be – svelte and beautiful. They also like
you just the way you are. Your job, therefore, is to
change and stay the same all at once. Good luck.

Mothers of fatties come in two varieties (yes, only two):
a. fat ones, and b. thin ones. When *you* are trying to
diet, FAT MOTHERS THINK THE FOLLOWING (CONFLICT-
ING) THOUGHTS – sometimes all at once:

1. It's *my* fault he/she is fat. Genes, you see. It's
   coded in the genes.

2. Don't blame *me*. I've always been careful about
   balanced meals.

3. *I* have a weight problem. I hope he/she slims
   down.

4. *I* have a weight problem. I'll feel resentful if
   he/she slims down.

5. The problem is, he/she *never stops* to eat
   properly.

6. The problem is, he/she *never stops* **eating**.

7. If only that child would *diet*!

8. That child is *starving* him/herself. (No wonder he/she catches colds!)

9. To be attractive, a girl doesn't have to be skinny as a model.

10. A few pounds thinner, and she'd be prettier than a model.

11. He/she should do it for him/herself.

12. The family would be so impressed!

It's easy to see that, if mum is on the heavy side, your efforts to slim arouse mixed emotions. She feels both supportive, and competitive. On the one hand, she'd be pleased as punch if you lost a few pounds, and brought home as many boyfriends as your cousin Eileen. On the other, you are a living rebuke to her ... rejecting the diet and lifestyle of earliest childhood, and implying by your actions that she:

1. overfed you – or fed you the wrong foods – as a child, and allowed you to become a tub

2. should take herself in hand, and do something about her *own* weight.

By way of contrast, THIN MOTHERS THINK THE FOLLOW-ING(CONFLICTING) THOUGHTS – sometimes all at once:

1. Pity he/she takes after *dad's* side of the family!

2. Don't blame *me*. I've always been careful about balanced meals.

3. A bit of extra weight is unimportant.

4. Surplus weight is a bit embarrassing.

5. He/she ought to exercise self-discipline. *I* do.

6. A young person should be able to eat what he/she likes!

7. I hope he/she diets, and sticks with it.

8. I hope he/she won't become anorexic.

9. After all . . . it's *character* that really counts.

10. Who cares if you're a 'nice person' when you're *fat*?

11. He/she will get more out of life *thin*.

12. Thinner than Eileen.

If you think *you* feel a sense of ambivalence and confusion about your spare padding . . . imagine how your *mother* feels! How is she to reconcile the conflicting maternal urges to nurture you and deprive you of food at the same time? Is she really meant to sit back (or even assist) while you systematically eliminate large parts of your body? She wants the best for you, but can't endure the accompanying pain. She knows you look perfect just as you are, but fears that others may be misled by your double chin. She's afraid that if she *encourages* your diet, you'll develop an eating disorder. She's afraid that if she *thwarts* your diet, you'll develop an eating disorder.

Furthermore, mum is only human – and therefore capable of feeling *threatened* by your regimen. Exemplary will-power in one person can serve as a rebuke to others. Does your diet imply that *she* should have the courage to starve, too? Or that she's too old to care? Or that she bears some responsibility for your weight, because she failed to instil proper eating habits? At a stroke, you've marginalized her, rejected her lifestyle, and spurned the banana custard you said you loved when you were six.

MOTHER'S WISDOM

In addition, mum is as baffled as you by the swings and shifts in 'expert' opinion on diet. She remembers when it was considered essential for 'good' mothers to provide children with three square meals a day. How is she to grapple with new recommendations for a few steamed vegetables, the minimum daily adult requirement of complex carbohydrate, plus some protein? It's enough to destroy anyone's nurturing instinct. Anyway, if you're one of *today's* gottabe skinnies, be aware that *yesterday's* mother does not always know best.

SO, *DO NOT* LISTEN TO YOUR MOTHER WHEN SHE SAYS:

1. **Eat, eat, it'll do you good.**
   It probably won't. (Or only if it's low in saturated fats, and high in fibre.)

2. **Feed a cold and starve a fever.**
   Better still – starve them both.

3. **Just cut out bread and potatoes, and you'll be fine.**
   Retain the bread and potatoes, but cut out the butter and you'll be fine.

4. **Always start the day with a cooked breakfast.**
   Start the day with no more than 250 cals. of
   complex carbohydrates. (Doesn't matter if they're
   hot or cold.)

5. **People need three square meals a day**.
   No, they don't.

6. **You're not *fat* . . . you're *well-built*.**
   You're fat.

7. **Mr/Miss Right will appreciate you just as you are**.
   Third division nerds will overlook your
   appearance.

8. **If you don't eat more than that, you'll waste away**.
   You're finally eating the right amount for effective
   weight loss. Go for it!

HONEY, LET'S SHRINK THE KIDS!
(*Mothering Strategies for the Nineties*)

A new generation of mothers can often learn from the
mistakes of the past. Young mums will, of course, be
gripped by age-old anxiety when Junior rejects his rusks.
But:

If you are a 'modern' mother, remember:

1. Babies do not have to be fat to be:

    a. cute, or
    b. healthy

When seated on the floor, they should *not* resemble a stack of Michelin tyres suspended over a nappy.

2. Children with a high fat and sugar intake may be storing up trouble for the future. Be aware of – and, if necessary, limit – intake of 'junk' and fried foods. Ditto the sugar in sweets, biscuits, carbonated drinks and squash. Do *not* allow your children to live on products made with artificial sweetener such as NutraSweet. Take time to read labels carefully.

3. Offer children food when they're *hungry* – not when they're bored or cranky. Beware of constantly promoting ice cream, candy or crisps as 'rewards' for good behaviour. Even the dimmest sprog will come to regard them as specially desirable, and ask for them constantly.

4. Be aware if your family has a history of heart disease. If so, be sure that your own and older children's cholesterol counts are checked regularly. Counts can be monitored with a simple blood test by your local G P.

5. Do not allow *food* to be the main outlet for your nurturing skills. There are, after all, plenty of other caring and creative pursuits. If you must *feed* something, try a rubber plant . . . or a parking meter.

9

FAT AND FAMILIES

The Well-Rounded Mother

Marriage, family life and weight gain need not go hand in hand . . . but they too often do. The slim-hipped young man who once washed his 501s at the launderette and ate on the run (if at all) marries, and enjoys the luxury of regular meals. Soon, he needs to be shoehorned into his old denims. The slender, Lycra-clad young woman sharing digs with three others who write their names on their yogurts becomes a wife. As she settles down, her body *changes*. Suddenly, she's 'mothershaped' . . . even when she's not pregnant.

Yes, it seems that the domestic bliss which we all desire can be *fattening*. Pity, really. Natural fatties, in particular, should beware the state of cud-chewing contentment which piles on pounds. It *is* possible to be 'married-with-children-and-a-nice-figure' . . . but it takes some planning. Husbands, wives and mothers should be aware of the potential ravages of FAT-THINK, and make every effort to *think thin*. The exchange of 'I dos' (or the birth of a child, or the first joint purchase from the Habitat catalogue) is not a cue to pig out.

HARRIED WITH CHILDREN

Pregnancy, of course, plays temporary havoc with the female form, stretching tummy forward, hip-bones sideways, and bosoms down. 'Getting your figure back' after the birth of baby can be hard work (it's often said that the last 5 pounds are sheer hell). Strict dieting should not, of course, be undertaken while pregnant or breast-feeding, except under a doctor's supervision. Nor, however, should you *abandon* all sense of control while 'nature takes its course'. Give in to your constant desire for sardines in hot fudge and you'll soon put on surplus weight – just as you would at any other time. (Fatties – even pregnant or nursing fatties – cannot rely exclusively on nature to get the balance right.)

In short, women at home should not let down their guard. It's plain to see that this is no time – nutritionally speaking – to relax. Nothing is 'over'. Things, in one sense, are just beginning. In order to retain feelings of self-esteem, plus a sense of order and control over life, it is vital to maintain your shape. Nothing will make you unhappier faster than the image of yourself as an over-blown *hausfrau*, with a wardrobe of once-glamorous clothes which don't fit, broken bits of Fisher-Price under-foot, damp crumbs of rusk in your hair, and regurgitated Cow and Gate down your (ample) front.

Yes, it *is possible* to *think thin* when you're a mother. Eating for two. Cooking for four. Worrying for six. Desperately wishing to be a size 8.

Here's the deal. Make up your mind from the start that you will never, *ever* invoke the *mother's excuse*. Strike it ruthlessly from your thoughts. It is fundamental FAT-THINK, and spells the beginning of the end. It will add pounds, and ultimately sabotage your happiness.

MOTHER'S EXCUSE:
I HAVE TO COOK MORE, SO I EAT MORE.

If you're at home with a family, prepare to take yourself firmly in hand. You are in danger of falling prey to your own proximity to the refrigerator. There you are, 'handling' food all day. Shopping for it. Storing it. Washing it and slicing it. Applying heat to it. Pulverizing it in food processors. Spooning it into a creature too small and weak to look after itself. Your husband.

As if that weren't enough, you clean up after it. Put it away. Then start again. Not surprisingly, your *own* food intake soon loses any direct connection it may once have had to *hunger*.

Day in the Life of a Housewife

The pitfalls are easy to spot – but hard to avoid. Few men are faced with the temptations involved in structuring a day around food preparation. The wonder is not that some women at home expand ... but that many stay trim.

THIN-THINK

Eating all day really spoils my appetite.

There are, however, a few ways of breaking the cook–eat cycle which has proved the undoing of many a stay-at-home mum:

1. Work out *your own* menu for the day. Know that you will have, say, Bran Flakes for breakfast, salad for lunch, and grilled fish (with the family) for dinner. Keep your rations 'discrete' in your own mind, and treat cooking for others as a *separate* job. Problems begin when the lines are blurred, and eating becomes more or less continuous. Do not *lose track* of your intake. Plan it every morning, and review it every night.

2. Try to spend regular periods each day *away from the house*. Shop – with your baby if necessary. Window shop. Visit friends (preferably ones who are short of food). Go to libraries or playgroups. If you're offered refreshment, accept only tea or coffee. Drink it with skimmed milk for preference, and without sugar.

3. If you can manage a part-time job or volunteer work – *do it*. It gives you a separate focus, encourages you to dress smartly, and re-establishes your sense of control. Most important – it puts several miles between you and your refrigerator.

4. *Rationalize cooking time.* When you cook for a baby –
or for your family – try to do so in 'batches'. If you're
making stew or a casserole, make a *big* one. Divide it
into portions, retaining only what you need immediately,
and freezing the rest. (You can't snack on something
frozen solid.) With luck, you won't have to cook again
for days!

REMEMBER:
TO COOK IS TO EAT

The less cooking you do – the less you actually handle
food – the less temptation there will be to put it in your
mouth. Reluctance to cook frequently does not make
you a third-rate mother. It makes you a *thin* mother.
(Also a smart one!) Reduce time spent in the kitchen,
and – as a bonus – you'll probably find that you begin
to enjoy your own food more. This is because the
palaver of daily preparation is a real appetite-killer,
which – paradoxically – can encourage you to *over-eat*.
(As Chief Cook, you find yourself sharing family meals
when you're not hungry . . . so it's hard to know when
you've had enough.)

SAMPLE SOLUTION: For a family of four, roast a 12 to 14
pound turkey – then **relax** for the next week. The kids
will think it's Christmas, and you can put a few low-fat
slices on pitta bread with salad.

5. Do not 'double eat'. If you're feeding a baby, feed the
baby. Then – when you can concentrate – feed yourself.
Separately. Do not finish a child's unwanted food. That's

what waste bins (or freezers) are for. You are *not* the family disposal. Children's leftovers are shopworn, unappetizing – and full of calories. Remember that you're not supposed to go on 'eating for two' *after* the baby's been born.

If you are trying to lose weight, you should aim to eat when you're comparatively relaxed. That way, you can monitor food intake, eat only as much as you need, and then *stop*. If you eat while preoccupied (with a child, for instance) it's easy to lose track.

6. Keep a bare cupboard. (Mother Hubbard had the right idea.) No one who dreams of wearing today's demanding fashions should ever tempt fate with a full larder. *To cook is to eat*. To purchase food is to cook. Don't chance it.

OK, OK. Any mother at home needs to keep supplies. But you needn't stock up as if you're expecting two years of nuclear winter. If it's *there*, chances are you'll eat it. If you're serious about losing weight, force yourself to reach for diet-friendly fruits and raw vegetables. Keep a giant pack of bacon crisps around, and it'll win every time.

7. Consider the advantages of buying *small amounts*. Received wisdom says that it's more economical to buy in 'bulk'. However:

   a. If you read labels carefully, you'll sometimes find that the large size is just as expensive as the small.

   b. Why invest spare cash in provisions, when it could be earning money on deposit?

   c. As a general rule, foods which are bought fresh
      – and often – are more compatible with THIN-
      THINK.

   d. Store large quantities of *any* food in the house,
      and you're bound to use *more* of it, *more*
      liberally, and *more* often.

8. Feel entirely free to throw old food – or mangled
family left-overs – away. No one (especially you) should
feel obliged to finish what's on the plate or in the fridge.
Stop thinking about how much that half-chewed lamb
chop would be welcomed in Somalia. You will not
materially help the Third World by expanding out of a
size 14.

This goes for the kids, too. Never force them to clean
their plates because you've cooked. Eating should be
associated with hunger ... not a misplaced sense of
obligation or guilt. Think several times before interfering
with a child's ability to regulate his or her own eating
habits.

9. *Cheat* at family cooking. If a recipe says, 'brown the
beef in oil before stewing it' – *don't*. Once a casserole is
complete, no one can tell whether or not cubes of meat
have been fried. *Don't* butter sandwich bread before
adding filling. (When you're eating, say, tuna and cucumber, who needs butter?) Use skimmed milk in cooking. They'll never notice, and you'll cut fat intake for
everyone.

10. Dieting mums should treat themselves as *separate* –
but *equal*. Establish a kind of nutritional apartheid. Remember that you cook things which *they* like ... so it's

also fine to prepare separate things which *you* need. If they're having burgers and chips, take the trouble to make yourself a cold pasta salad instead.

11. *Think* before you *serve*. Give yourself smaller portions than you serve to your husband. And don't feel deprived! Chances are that you weigh less than he does. The idea is to keep it that way.

12. Pay attention during family meals. Concentrate. Know when you've come to the end of your food allowance. The sheer momentum of family life 'Kylie, you're about to spill that milk!' can make you take your eye off the ball. Absent-minded eating adds calories – and you don't have the chance to enjoy them going down.

13. Use *restaurants* wherever possible. Not pretentious, 'special occasion' places, but modestly priced, 'family style' ones. There are important advantages to fatties in regular eating out:

> a. The less you handle and cook food at home, the less you'll eat.
>
> b. Restaurants can prepare different dishes for different people, and will easily cater for your diet ('plainly-grilled fish, hold the butter') without inconveniencing your family.

It is in many ways *easier* to diet in restaurants – despite the temptations of a fine menu – *because*:

> a. Restaurant portions are limited. There is no opportunity to go back for seconds.
>
> b. You are less 'relaxed' at restaurants than you would be at home, and therefore tend to eat

less. You're unlikely to undo waistbands or belts to 'make room for more'.

c. Today, many restaurants are happy for you to *share* courses (for example, with a child). This has the double advantage of keeping costs down – and your portions small. Besides, simply *being* in a restaurant endows any meal with a sense of occasion – which shifts the emphasis away from food. 'Look, Brian. Did you see how short her dress is? Brian? *Brian!*'

Don't fall into the trap of regarding a meal out as an excuse for a gastronomic blow-out. Treat restaurants more as a 'resource', using them to cater for your diet needs. Ask waiters to have the skin removed from chicken, and for vegetables to be steamed without butter. Don't order dessert. Instead, content yourself with a nice, sophisticated cappuccino, and some people-watching. See that girl with the magnificent body and the tight dress? Get through the evening without weakening, and *you'll* be able to wear one, too!

Feel no guilt about either:

a. the expenditure involved (not much more, if you're careful, than eating at home) or

b. the perceived self-indulgence. (Consider it an investment in the figure you've always wanted; more fun – and much healthier – than shelling out for containers of disgusting meal replacements.)

Any pastime which increases eating pleasure without adding calories is worth a few bob.

Above all, remember:

IF GOD WANTED WOMEN TO COOK, HE WOULDN'T HAVE INVENTED RESTAURANTS.

With luck, you can get through *years* of marriage without ever applying heat to food.

In short, culinary obligations need *not* come between female fatties and the figures to which they aspire. Plan things correctly, train husband and children, and there's nothing to stand in your way. As a bonus, it's a fair bet that your improved eating habits may rub off on them. Even if they resist. (Especially if they don't notice.)

Film star Shelley Winters – who disliked animals – was famous for the one-liner, 'Never have anything that *eats*.' She probably meant families, too.

10
MONTHLY PERIODS
'Dietus Interruptus'

The following scenario may sound familiar. Your diet is
working at last! Weight loss – agonizingly slow to start
– gathers momentum and pace. With each passing day,
you feel more optimistic, more excited. Can it be that the
goal is achievable – the shape of your dreams just a few
low-cal weeks away?

Only if you take care to avoid *dietus interruptus*. As your
slimming programme makes progress, it's surprising
how events conspire against you, and get in the way.
Booby-traps come in many forms:

Potential Diet-Busters

1. A holiday in France or Italy, where the food is
   sensational. As if that weren't bad enough,
   waiters deliver baskets of croissants to your
   room each morning.

2. A split with your boy/girlfriend – or any
   emotional upheaval which makes you 'eat to
   forget'. (In the case of hard-core fatties, this can
   include the death of a goldfish.)

3. An invitation to tour the Sara Lee factory.

4. A surprise birthday party for *you*, where it seems churlish to turn down your own cake.

5. Christmas, the week before Christmas, and the week after Christmas, when the entire nation hibernates, surrounded by leftovers.

And – most important –

6. THE ONSET OF A MENSTRUAL PERIOD.

Men have problems of their own with diets . . . but they don't have to deal with a natural cycle guaranteed to halt progress every twenty-eight days. There can be little doubt that monthly periods are inimical to weight loss. No wonder women conclude that nature *intended* them to be fat!

It's not just the week *of* the period when things are bad. There are two miserable weeks *before* and *after*. What it boils down to is that – for most females – there are only about *ten good dieting days* each month.

For a week or so prior to menstruation, you feel ugly, spotty, and *fat*. Naturally, this undermines determination to exercise restraint in order to become thin and beautiful. When you feel bloated, it is more difficult to deprive yourself. The inclination is to surrender, and go completely to seed.

'Seed' is not far away. Everything is wrong. Observed in profile, your protuberant tum can be seen fighting your waistbands . . . and winning. You're retaining enough water to irrigate Southern California. Your temper is foul – made worse because you're unusually hungry. You crave sugar in industrial quantities, would kill for a Mars Bar, and – if nothing better presents itself – will eat spoonfuls of kiddie-style chocolate syrup straight from the plastic bear.

Overcome by a kind of food hysteria, you can't shovel it in fast enough. You're so ravenous that your hands shake as they tear at nourishment. You inadvertently bite the insides of your cheeks, because you're chewing too furiously to make sure they're well clear. You possess as much sense of self-control as a shark in a feeding frenzy.

VICIOUS CYCLE

Too many women – perhaps *most* women – find themselves in this sorry state each month. The week before the period is a dieting write-off . . . the days of the period are just plain grotty . . . and it's five days after menstruation before body tissues finally release excess fluid. Only then does cutting calories seem to produce results in the form of weight loss.

There's a brief 'window' of time in which to make a tiny *smidge* of progress. Struggle, starve for days, and lose a pound. Then – overnight – you're up *three*. It's time for another period . . . and you're a human sponge.

Mother Nature is a bitch. As a woman, she clearly has it in for females. Just look around! As the years pass, most of them inexorably widen, their girlish shapes giving way to that dumpy, frumpy, waistless middle-aged figure known as 'matronly'. Nature's little booby-traps – periods, pregnancies, and finally, menopause – take their toll, each adding 'just a bit' of extra weight. Determination to remain slim is defeated by a lifetime of hormone surges, cramps, ovulation, pills, fibroids, prolapses ... and finally, hot flushes.

There are, of course, the Britt Eklands of this world – the Joan Collinses and the Jane Fondas – whose youthful and gravity-defying shapes seem frozen in time. (Somewhere deep in their filofaxes is the name of a personal trainer I'd like to meet.) Frankly, the well-preserved should be given full credit. Beyond a certain age, metabolic rate slows. With each successive period, retained fluid is harder to shed, tummies are more flaccid, weight-loss goals more remote. As women age, their fat cells seem to lie in wait, *willing* them to weaken:

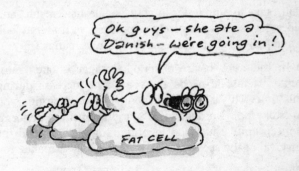

Feel free to murder the next person who observes that 'nature is wonderful'. Nature *isn't* wonderful. Nature is a sod. Nature *wants* women to be fat. Nature is very busy making us menstruate, bear children or breast-feed – and a thousand other things which generally wreck our ability to squeeze into the latest Armani.

Anyway, if nature's so bloody marvellous, why do we crave cream cakes and fry-ups and other things which doctors say will kill us? Wouldn't it have been more efficient to endow us all with a natural yearning for *fibre*? When was the last time you heard anyone say, 'Hey, I'd kill for some oat bran'? No. It's a sad fact that successful dieting – and staying slim – is, for most women, a question of working *against* nature, and showing it who's boss.

Here's what you have to do to beat the VICIOUS CYCLE:

1. When pre-period bloating begins, and you feel famished and supremely unattractive, you should temporarily *change your objective*. Do not aim for weight *loss*. Until menstruation is over, concentrate on *maintenance*.

Don't give in, and fester in your baggiest sweatshirt and oldest jeans. Dress as nicely as possible, so that you look – and *feel* – in control. Prepare for hunger pangs.

2. In the week before a period, hunger is often most acute. Metabolic needs show a slight increase during this time. This is rotten old Mother Nature urging you to 'stoke up'. No doubt this 'gorging' instinct performs some primitive function in promoting fertility, and the survival of the species. Unfortunately, it also makes you *fat*.

Continue your 'damage containment' strategy for the duration of menstruation. If ravenous, *eat* – but try to cram in 'OK' foods, such as raw vegetables, fruit, tomato juice, plain very low-fat yogurt, and wholemeal bread. If you're overcome by an irresistible urge for sweets, you'll find it can be satisfied surprisingly well with a small glass of freshly-squeezed orange juice, or a dried apricot or prune. Sure, you'd rather have a Kit Kat ... but that's not the point, is it?

3. Remember that your (temporary) new objective is not to *lose* weight during your period, but merely to avoid *gaining*. (The last part is remarkably difficult, since you are hungry enough to eat a town the size of Croydon at a single sitting.) When it's over, and excess body fluid has been shed, you should ideally return to your pre-period weight. Then, with assiduous dieting for the next two to three weeks, you can make real progress. If, on the other hand, you allow yourself to store extra fat during a period, you'll spend the two to three weeks getting back to square one. This is truly soul-destroying. Maintaining your weight through a period is a test of supreme will-power, and is probably what is meant by 'the curse'. For female fatties, it's also the real secret of staying ahead of the game.

4. Do not be afraid to drink lots of water during a period for fear of retaining it. Water actually helps to 'flush' the system, and aids urinary function. It will do much to relieve troublesome constipation, plus the general feeling of pre-menstrual congestion. Taken with food, it helps to satisfy hunger by producing a 'full' feeling without adding calories. *Do* avoid excess salt, which can encourage tissues to retain even more water.

5. Be prepared for the occasional *period of record inflation*. Every so often, you'll notice a worrying effect around the time of menstruation. Suddenly, unaccountably, you begin to gain weight. You're not eating any more than usual. You may even be cutting back, limiting intake to

around 1,000 to 1,200 calories a day. Nothing is more shocking – or dismaying – than watching the scale climb relentlessly in spite of your best efforts. The gain can be substantial, running to 4 or 5 pounds in a single week (try *losing* that much, even on a starvation diet!). Your weight is like a currency in free-fall, except in reverse . . . reminding you that things can go up as well as down.

No one seems sure why such extraordinary pre-period weight increases take place. Doctors talk about fluid retention, and look doubtful when you insist you've been dieting strictly. It's all too frustrating for words . . . especially when you've felt hungry for *weeks*. This is your Beechers' Brook – the most difficult hurdle you'll have to cross. If you've been eating very little, try to eat even less. Alleviate hunger with fruits and vegetables. Ruthlessly cut all flab-fodder (sugar, alcohol, fats) from your diet. Exercise more. This is a lesson in *diet crisis management*. Most of all – hang in there for a few days. Much of the gain should prove temporary, and disappear a week or so after the end of menstruation. Meanwhile, look around for new calorie cuts to make – however marginal. Do you *really need* that tiny teaspoon of sugar on your Special K? How about the evening glass of wine with dinner? The idea is to avoid giving your body any spare calories to store. With a bit of luck, you'll ride out the crisis.

6. *Fight lethargy*. The week before a period, you may feel unusually tired . . . draggy and irritable. It's probably Mother bloody Nature again, encouraging you to lie still and gain even *more* weight. Confound her if you can. Keep busy. Clear a closet, catch up on filing, take the

dog for a walk. It's also important to feel as attractive as possible (difficult with pendulous breasts, sagging stomach, and a pimple blossoming in a prominent place). A boost to your appearance can help to revive flagging determination.

Shopping for clothes may not work, since your body's not at its best. Instead, try changing your hair colour, or having a long overdue manicure. Visit the dentist for a clean-and-polish ... or choose new frames for your reading glasses. Focus on hair, nails, eyeballs and teeth – the only features you have which are *visible* – but don't get fat.

11
BOYFRIENDS, GIRLFRIENDS AND FAT
Can the Well-Padded Find Love?
or
SEX AND FAT
Can You Hold in Your Tummy, and Still Reach Climax?

It is no doubt true that men are more tolerant and forgiving of the female body shape than women themselves. Many are the tales of girls who – following passionate love-making – rise naked and retreat *backwards* from the room, so he won't see their tummies in profile. Their preference for dim lighting has less to do with romance than self-consciousness about spare padding. They choose erotic positions which deftly conceal the size of their thighs.

This self-critical approach not only inhibits real pleasure in love-making but blinds women to the fact that most men in an advanced state of arousal are fairly *goal-oriented*, and not apt to be dwelling on hip measurements. Otherwise sensible and intelligent women are beyond reassurance on this point. And, no wonder! He may *claim* to adore your 'curves' ... but, when a girl built like a supermodel sashays by, flat of tum and sleek

of thigh, his knees give way. Ask him why, and he says it's not because she's thin ... it's because she 'looks great'. Being female (and a higher form of life), you understand that she looks great because she's *thin*.

Women constantly 'beat up on' themselves, and judge themselves harshly. They draw no comfort from clear evidence that men can – and *do* – love imperfect figures. Were this not so, the species could hardly have survived to the year 2,000. Many's the fellow who positively prefers a body more curvaceous than the lean, mean (pared down) shapes to which women aspire. Asked to choose between Audrey Hepburn and Marilyn Monroe, he'd go for Marilyn every time.

However, the point is that that's not the point. We're not dieting for *them*, are we? Goodness, no (though a love affair is a swell incentive to weight loss). We're dieting for *ourselves*. We are, after all, creatures of the nineties. In touch with our own needs. In possession of the right magazines. Aware that women must 'seize control' of life in order to achieve self-esteem. That we need to 'feel beautiful' in order to shed inhibitions, and experience full erotic satisfaction. That we need to 'love ourselves' before we can expect love from others. To put it more simply – we need to feel *thin*.

GUY-THINK

The men who'd like a handful of Marilyn see things differently. The sight of your dimpled buttocks does not kill passion. Different criteria. His requirements are simple. He wants his partner to be shapely, yes . . . but most of all, he wants her *available*. It is less important that you should be *thin*, than that you should be *there*.

The problem is that few women (young or old) involved in physical relationships are at peace with their bodies. Craving constant reassurance, they test their long-suffering partners to the limits, provoke them, and generally drive them mad.

LOVE HURTS

Apart from being at the sharp end of women's insecurities about shape, men are lucky. In general, they enjoy a far easier and more casual relationship with food. Ever watched a starry-eyed, dating couple in a restaurant? He's busy putting away a dripping, half-pound bacon cheeseburger, as the love-light shines from his eyes. She – equally besotted – is pushing a salad around her plate.

To consume food would, for her, seem somehow wrong. It would create the unromantic impression that – faced with his irresistible charms – she's still able to *eat*. Being in love means never getting to say you're hungry.

Her reluctance to take nourishment signals other things as well. That her interest in him is stronger than the Life Force. That she is the weaker partner, in need of male care and protection. That she is feminine, needing only small amounts of food to live. That she is light as a feather, and would be easy to work with in bed.

He, meanwhile, is free to trough away with gusto, appearing strong and 'butch'. It is remarkable and interesting to observe that men, on dates, eat exactly as they do when their mothers feed them at home. Matter-of-factly. Without restraint, inhibition, or embarrassment. Lots.

IN LOVE

SHE is 'in love'. This gives her an instant desire to shrink in size. He is 'in love'. The last thing he wants is to be *smaller*. In any way. On the contrary, he is 'stoking up', ready for action. Conquests require an intake of calories. A man's gotta eat what a man's gotta eat.

She Won't Eat in Front of Him Because:

1. It makes her feel fat and slob-like.

2. People look ugly when they chew.

3. Spinach can stick in your teeth.

4. All the lip gloss will rub off.

5. It's impossible to enjoy it much while he's watching, anyway.

6. Her jeans are too tight.

7. The smell of food on your breath is a real turn-off. (He feels no similar inhibitions about his side-order of enchiladas with jalepeno peppers).

8. She wants to seem more interested in him than the menu.

9. Everyone knows that girls with great figures just pick at food.

10. She wants to feel *thin* in case they make love.

As a result, she's secretly *starving*.

You can tell when they order dessert. He does not take his gaze from his beloved's (by now pinched) face as he tells the waitress:

> 'I'll-have-a-piece-'a-chocolate-cake-one-scoop-'a-vanilla-ice-cream-with-hot-fudge-sauce-hold-the-whipped-cream.'

Their eyes remain locked. She does not relax her adoring smile . . . but – at the sound of his words – begins slowly to drool.

TRUE LOVE MEANS SHARING DESSERT

She dreams of a body like Marla Maples'. But, when dessert is served, she can contain herself no longer. Compulsively, she grips her fork. He, feeling replete and mellow, does not notice as she slowly slides her implement beneath his fond gaze, and into his plate. She sneaks small, blissful bites, pretending to eat absent-mindedly. He, in the time-honoured 'guy' way, stabs at automatic forkfuls while continuing to talk, scarcely noticing what he eats. She savours every forbidden mouthful, secretly hoping that he won't reach across to hold *both* her hands in his, thus impeding the action of her fork.

She is by now so hungry, that she could eat *him*. She is beginning to look forward to getting home, so she can *eat like crazy*. He, on the other hand, is much restored . . . and beginning to feel sexy. When at last they're alone, she can't concentrate. His caresses fail to charm. Distracted, she lays back and thinks of cheeseburgers.

MAN'S WORLD

Yes, it's often true that love hurts. But, *dieting* hurts even more. So, when it comes to weight-watching, it is indeed a man's world. This is not to deny that there are many men with problems: statistics show that, in Britain, between one third and one half of middle-aged men are overweight. (This is clearly undesirable from a medical standpoint, since men are at greater risk of heart disease than women.) But – in terms of *appearance* – men enjoy the advantage. They needn't be *skinny* in order to look good. Spare padding will not be exposed in stretchy, skin-tight clothes. Unless a man is truly tubby, he'll simply be perceived as 'solid', or 'well-built'. The lucky chap can hide a multitude of sins under the jacket of a double-breasted suit.

It is often claimed that women are 'domestic' creatures. The truth is that men are more easily domesticated than women. The cool dude who spent his twenties cruising the night in search of blondes, adjusts surprisingly well to carpet-slippered home comforts. He likes regular meals. In fact, he likes *any* kind of meals. He burns fewer calories, since he no longer needs to chase girls. He quickly discovers that food – once taken on the run – is best eaten sitting down. Preferably while watching telly. He is getting *fat*.

In some ways, he doesn't care. He's comfy. Anyway . . . he has no wish to be skinny. He harbours just one misgiving. Sport. What if he's asked to play a game of football or squash? What if he goes on holiday, and wants to appear poolside in bathing shorts? How will he look to other fellows as he strips off in the locker room? This is a worry even if he hasn't been *near* a locker room for thirty years. It is probably his best (possibly his *only*) incentive to diet. 'Jock-strap' motivation.

It's a fact that the automatic link between food and guilt – so familiar to women – is less well-established in the male mind. The average man is still – gastronomically speaking – primitive. He eats when he's hungry. He stops when he's full. He doesn't torture himself. He selects food that he likes, and (unless under strict doctor's orders) rejects the stuff he doesn't much care for. Especially salad.

Every so often – when his protruding tummy blocks his view of his flies – he resolves to 'get fit'. In a burst of enthusiasm, he does fifty press-ups on the bedroom floor, just to prove to himself that he still *can*. Thus reassured (and physically shattered), he reverts to slob-mode, and carries on as normal. Only his wife suffers. His sex drive disappears for a month.

REAL MEN DON'T EAT SALADS

When he finally decides to diet seriously, the average man confronts the task more directly, carrying less

emotional baggage than the average woman. His motivation and will-power are fine, and he is potentially an
effective dieter. Nutritionally, however, he is a novice
. . . a babe-in-the-woods when it comes to understanding
which foods are low in fats. He is not used to satisfying
hunger with a few watery lettuce leaves and an apple,
and needs female guidance. If he's lucky, he'll have a
wife, mother or girlfriend who can advise, and perhaps
provide appropriate food as well. Otherwise (since the
only thing he hates more than *eating* salad is *preparing*
it) he's stuck trying to follow his calorie-controlled eating
plan at a local branch of Burger King.

The woman in his life has been through all this many
times before. Dieting, she warns, is 'hell'. She knows
from experience that you've got to suffer and starve for
weeks before weight drops so much as an ounce.
Imagine, then, her mixture of pride and chagrin as her
man succeeds where she has so often failed. *Because* –
and this is the single most infuriating thing about sons,
lovers and husbands – **diets work for men**. The male
metabolism, accustomed as it is to dealing with *big*
things (McDonalds double fries, a couple of pints of lager
and buffalo-on-toast) shifts into 'overdrive' when a
lonely bit of raw carrot gurgles down the pipe. His
digestive system – capable of pulverising skip-loads of
rubbish – signals 'red alert'. Two days later, he's lost a
stone. Worst of all, he has never known the true meaning of suffering.

FAT 'STATS'

When it comes to fat, statistics are revealing. The 1990 Dietary and Nutritional Survey of British Adults, which looked at men and women between the ages of sixteen and sixty-four – concludes that men are *more* likely to be overweight than women. Forty-five per cent of men were found to be too heavy, as compared with 36 per cent of women. (In the category of 'middle-aged' men, nearly 50 per cent needed to reduce.) Men were comparatively slow to take action, but – once started – stuck with their diets *longer* than women (an average of ten weeks to the women's six and a half).

What the report *doesn't* say is what every female in the land already knows: a man can stick to a diet longer than a woman *because*:

1. A woman is helping him. She is probably preparing his meals and adapting his diet, instead of obstructing his efforts.

2. He is encouraged by seeing *results*. After ten weeks, he is stones lighter than when he started.

The average female diet may, of course, be shorter at six and a half weeks simply because she has less weight to lose. Chances are, though, that she will be *less successful* at losing it. This is *because*:

1. He resists *her* diet. (She's boring about it/his meals are no longer fun.)

2. She becomes discouraged when weeks of fasting produce slow results – or *no* results.

She quickly becomes a serial dieter. She starts and stops again and again. Her diets may last for only six and a half weeks . . . but she goes on six of them for every one of his. Soon, the exercise becomes self-defeating. No matter who she is, or what her circumstances, she can list compelling reasons why she *can't diet*.

IN THE 'WOMEN ARE NEVER HAPPY' CATEGORY

I Can't Diet Because:

1. I broke up with my boyfriend. There's no man in my life. I eat to forget.

2. I eat to anaesthetize my pain, loneliness and depression.

3. I stuff myself as an expression of low self-esteem.

4. Compulsive eating is a metaphor for the emotional hunger I feel.

5. I eat because I'm *single*.

I Can't Diet Because:

1. I'm stuck at home. He doesn't notice how I look. I eat because I might as well.

2. I eat because I have to cook.

3. I eat what they eat, and they won't eat salads.

4. I binge because I'm only a homemaker, and lack the sense of separate identity that comes with a career.

5. I eat because I'm *married*.

12
'COMING OUT': HOW TO DIET IN RESTAURANTS

Most people regard restaurants as palaces of irresistible temptation, where diets are temporarily suspended as good intentions confront chocolate mousse – and both disappear. It needn't be so. Restaurants – when properly used – can be of real help to slimmers. In any case: it's useful to know how to dine out without giving in ... particularly if you've occasion to use restaurants frequently. Or just *like* them. Bad enough that you have to lose weight. Why deny yourself the pleasure of eating out?

THIN-THINK IN RESTAURANTS:

First rule of thumb: before ordering, *decide your intentions*. You only get TWO choices:

1. I will restrict calories enough to continue *losing* weight.

2. I will temporarily put my diet on 'hold'. I will eat enough to *maintain* weight, without actually gaining.

Clearly, if you are dining with close friends or family, you are free to pursue the first option. Nor should you feel sorry for yourself. It's pleasant, after all, just to be out . . . to dress up, people-watch, and share a sense of occasion. There's no need to eat yourself stupid at the same time.

If you choose option two, you may wish to keep a low profile, in order to avoid inhibiting others. No problem! Maintenance diets can be easily followed without fear of discovery.

The difference between the options is largely a question of degree. If you're dieting hard – and don't care who knows it – you can eat very little, and skip a course or two. By contrast, a 'maintenance' diet is an exercise in damage limitation. It allows you to eat your way through the menu, but – by choosing carefully – to avoid gaining weight. Both options stop miles short of a full-scale blow-out. Here are a few handy hints:

STEPPING OUT

1. If everyone else is having a pre-prandial 'aperitif', order a mineral water with a slice of fresh lemon or lime.

2. Feel free to have the proffered roll or piece of french bread before the meal. (You're probably starved, anyway.) But, limit yourself to one, and eat it without butter.

3. For a 'starter' – if nothing more interesting presents itself – choose one of the following:

    a. a slice of plain melon (say 'no' to Parma ham)

    b. half a grapefruit (no sugar)

    c. a glass of tomato juice (spiked with a dash of tabasco or Worcester sauce, some lemon juice and fresh pepper)

    d. fresh, steamed asparagus (no butter, but a splash or two of soy sauce)

    e. a plain mixed salad (no creamy dressings; moisten with a few drops of olive oil and vinegar, or plain balsamic vinegar, or a sprinkling of lemon juice)

    f. clear soup, consommé, or vegetable soup (nothing thickened with cream). Minestrone is fine, but don't add grated Parmesan. If you order onion soup, remove the cheese.

4. Cut your main course in *half*. Every restaurant in the Western world serves at least twice as much as a dieter needs to support life. This is true whether you've ordered lean meat, chicken or fish. If you can *share* an entree with someone (a child, for instance) so much the better. If not, simply interfere with the uneaten portion a bit. Break it up, and spread it around the plate. Bury it under the garnish if necessary.

Don't be inhibited by waiters and waitresses who clear the table and look worried by the remaining food. 'Was everything all right, sir?' No need to share with them details of your diet strategy. Just say 'wonderful, thanks,' and leave it at that.

Remember that many nutritionists claim that weight-reduction diets work most effectively when you limit yourself to 3 to 4 ounces of animal protein (meat, chicken or fish) per day. That's a *very small* portion.

5. Ask for cooked vegetables to be steamed or boiled (or grilled, if the restaurant is groovy) and served without butter.

6. Do not eat potatoes which are cooked in fat (fried, sautéed, or tin-roasted) or are mixed with cream or cheese. A really good bet is a baked or 'jacket' potato, which should be served *without* butter or sour cream. Cut it in two, and eat only half. *Do* eat the skin, which contains extra vitamin C, and provides useful roughage.

7. Pasta cooked in boiling water is diet-friendly, as long as you do not choose shapes stuffed with pork, cheese or meat (certain varieties of ravioli, cannelloni or tortelloni, for example). Plain, wholemeal pasta is to be preferred. Once again, portions should be kept small; no more than one and a half to two cups of uncooked pasta to be prepared as a main dish. (Try a mixed salad on the side.)

Pasta should be eaten *only* with tomato sauce (or marinara sauce, which is usually a spicier version of the same thing – but may contain seafood, so it pays to check). No cream sauces, butter, pesto or Bolognese. Fresh tomato and basil sauce is a good choice. Sorry, *no cheese* – not even a touch of grated Parmesan, which tastes terrif, but is a real diet-buster. Also, no sneaky inclusions in the pasta, like bits of ham, lobster, shellfish or bacon – though fresh vegetables are fine, so long as they haven't been cooked in butter or oil.

Tricky, this diet business. A truly dedicated slimmer needs to be as alert and vigilant as an airport sniffer dog checking luggage for traces of illicit substances. *Fat* is, if you like, the nutritional version of Semtex. Often undetectable. Potentially destructive.

8. Rice is fine for dieters, but should be plainly cooked (steamed or boiled) with no added fats. Brown or wild rice – cooked the same way – is a nice variation on the theme.

9. **Drink thin**. Mineral water can (and should) be drunk throughout your meal. Alcohol – if you are genuinely dieting – must be strictly limited. Don't even *think* about beer, Guinness, or other high-calorie tipples. If, on occasion, you do drink, choose a glass of the driest white wine available, and finish only *half* the glass. Depending upon size, one glass can set you back around 100 calories, which uses up a disproportionate chunk of your limited daily allowance. You'll find that half a glass (40 to 50 calories) takes the 'edge' off, makes you feel that you've 'had a drink', and – once you get used to it – seems very satisfactory.

Beware of fruit juices. They may be labelled 'fresh' or 'pure' or 'no sugar added' – but this can be misleading, and the drinks may still be relatively high in calories. Fresh orange juice, for example, naturally contains sugar. Even if no more is added, you're probably taking in 80 calories per medium-sized glass. Ditto apple juice, or pineapple juice. Unsweetened grapefruit juice tends to be slightly lower – and tomato juice is perhaps the best diet drink of all: filling, and only 20 to 30 calories per medium-sized glass. (Do watch the sodium content if you're trying to cut down on salt.) Feel free to add a dash of tabasco, Worcester sauce or lemon, for 'kick' without calories.

Eliminate soft drinks from your menu. Colas, squash, lemonade and other fizzy drinks are diet-wreckers at up to 200 calories per shot. Why *drink* yourself fat?

Do not fall back on 'diet' colas, with one or no calories per can. These do nothing to help you break bad habits, and – according to doctors – may actually increase your appetite for sugary foods.

Water, water everywhere is the answer. At least six medium-sized glasses a day will help you to feel fuller and more satisfied, aid digestion – and generally 'keep things moving' so you *feel* thinner.

10. Simple rule of thumb: 'pass' on dessert. Instead, opt for a (sugarless but fashionable) espresso or cappuccino. If you prefer ordinary 'white' coffee or decaf, request skimmed or semi-skimmed milk in place of cream (or the vacuum-sealed 'milk substitute' which proves that even *food-free* products can be fattening).

If, on the other hand, you are entertaining an important client who's a serious trencherman, and definitely 'up' for a third course, keep him (or her) company with fresh fruit from the trolley . . . strawbs, raspberries, fresh pineapple, etc. Just say 'no' to sugar and cream.

If you're with family or close friends, remember that *desserts are made for sharing.* If everyone's weight-watching, get *one* sweet for the table, and content yourself with a bite or two as it orbits in your direction. Sharing makes self-control easier than you may think . . . and

FAT-THINK IN RESTAURANTS

The sweet trolley looks sensational. Profiteroles to die for.

Nothing for me, thanks. No, really.

Diets are miserable. I feel so left out.

Bet your creme caramel tastes great. Of course, you can afford it. You're *thin*.

Oh, sorry. Do I seem irritable?

Home at last.

I deserve consolation. Perhaps a Jaffa Cake.

THIN-THINK IN RESTAURANTS

Oh, goody. Time for dessert.

Anyone want to share?

One hot fudge sundae, 4 spoons.

Umm. Divine. Just one more bite, then it's Nigel's turn.

Waiter . . . I'd like my coffee now, please.

I am gonna look so gorgeous in that new lycra dress . . .

you'll never get fat on the tiny amounts you can snatch from a moving pudding.

Best of all, this arrangement makes you part of the 'gang'. One of the worst aspects of dieting is the sense of isolation and deprivation which wannabe skinnies feel. Everyone else is sharing a pleasant 'eating experience'. You are left out. Miserable and lonely, sorry for yourself, you soon break your fast. Not so, under this 'take a bite' arrangement.

Shed the flabbo psychology which moans: 'if I have *one* bite, I won't be able to stop!' That's FAT-THINK. Your thought-process should go as follows: 'If I have a bite or two of the black forest gateau/apple pie, I'll know how it tastes. I'll be part of the shared experience. That's just as satisfying as eating the whole slice. If I eat the whole slice, it will soon be over – just like the two little bites. Only I'll be fatter. And I'll *still* want more!' Far better to limit the damage to two small bites – and no regrets tomorrow.

13
FATTIES VS. FOOD: 'EATING THE ENEMY'

In their relentless quest for slim, trim bodies, aspiring skinnies of both sexes – doctors warn – are losing their ability to cope normally with *food*. Women, as ever, are at particular risk. The theory is that, in Western nations – where food supplies are plentiful, basic survival is assured, and a 'gourmet' snack is available at every street corner – we've 'lost touch' with our bodies' needs. The direct link between hunger, food and satisfaction has been broken . . . often with alarming results.

We no longer get hungry, *eat*, feel satisfied, *stop*. Instead, we self-censor. We deny, reject, fast, weaken, give in, binge, suffer guilt and self-hatred (which we associate directly with food) – then repeat the same destructive cycle again. When we're *hungry* (which is the last thing many of us want to be) *eating* is the last thing we want to do. The body's natural rhythms are disrupted, its needs ignored. Pretty soon, we're weak and head-achy from self-inflicted starvation . . . or unaccountably stuffing ourselves when we feel no real desire for food.

Female fatties are particularly pitiful creatures. Obsessed with our own appearance, we aspire to a 'perfect' body shape and size, frequently despising the one we have. Mesmerized by images of the ultra-thin and famous

(dreaming perhaps, of the black-clad, spider-legged model on the packet of Wolford tights), we vow to limit ourselves to small amounts of low-fat foods – then eat heaps of high-fat junk. Or, alternatively ... *nothing*. Soon, we develop a troubled relationship with most forms of nourishment.

Why Women Still Can't Cope with Food
(Julia Buckroyd, *Cosmopolitan* magazine, British edition, September 1989)

> Studies show that at least 50 per cent of women don't eat properly. Eating disorders range from being unable to leave a thing on their plates, to spending time in a vicious cycle of bingeing and

vomiting. There are women who use laxatives to keep their weight under control, while others scarcely eat enough to keep themselves alive, despite constant feelings of nausea, light-headedness and weakness.

It seems as though women (and some men, too) have lost the art of balancing what they eat with their actual physical needs, and are turning to food as a way of dealing with crises in their personal lives.

These days, we're all aware of the dangers of food abuse and compulsive dieting. But, consider the female dilemma! On the one hand, we're dazzled with images of sensational-looking supermodels, starved to perfection. On the other, we're warned against any attempt to perform this feat at home.

No wonder we're covered in cellulite and confusion. Our bookshelves groan with works like Susie Orbach's *Fat Is a Feminist Issue* and Naomi Wolf's *The Beauty Myth* – which provide a selection of rationales for *not dieting at all*. Every newspaper and women's magazine features the latest designer collections, while reminding us that women are victims of men, the fashion industry or sexual politics. That we eat (or don't eat) in order to remove ourselves from the sexual arena. That we stuff (or starve) to anaesthetize the pain of bad relationships. That Oprah Winfrey and Roseanne Barr are overweight because they come from dysfunctional families. That women 'binge' to assuage the emotional hunger they feel. That they are encouraged to 'fast' by cynical men who wish to keep them weak. In other words ... that

chronic self-imposed starvation undermines the potential strength and power of women. No kidding. Tell us about it.

In short, the whole area of diet and weight loss – particularly as it relates to women – has become a political hot potato. (No butter.) None of which stops the majority of us from wishing to be *thinner*. Somehow, the sight of Cindy Crawford in a bathing suit carries more clout than all the well-reasoned polemic, and nutritional debate. Very frustrating for those who wish to save us from ourselves.

Slimming can, of course, be carried too far. And no one denies that unreasonable pressures are brought to bear upon women. But, today's dieters (a category which now includes most women, and lots of men) are a fairly sophisticated lot. They know that it is possible to change eating habits without dire consequences if they approach weight loss sensibly. They also realize that a certain level of food fixation 'goes with the territory'. It has become *normal*. (This is not to be confused with the unhealthy compulsion which sends fifteen-year-olds to hospital suffering from self-inflicted malnutrition, or ageing movie stars to the Betty Ford Clinic for Beverly Hills fettucini abusers.) But it's a fact that any natural fatty who succeeds, over the years, in maintaining a slim figure walks a fine line. There's a permanent balance to be struck between commendable will-power, and food obsession.

POLITICALLY 'CORRECT'

Food is not our only problem. The fact is that life today demands self-discipline in many areas. We're not to eat or drink too much, drive too fast, or smoke *at all*. Most sexual activity is out. The only thing we're allowed to do *lots* of is exercise. The art of self-denial, it seems, is part of the health and fitness revolution. It is also

compatible with the 'New Age' nineties frame of mind
. . . lean, pared down and 'environmentally sound'. Dieting is 'green', if you think about it, since a slender body
is proof that you partake sparingly of the world's dimin-
ishing food resources. (It's a thought, anyway – and a
rationale for admiring Yasmin Le Bon.) *Fat* is greedy; a
tell-tale sign that you've cornered a scarce commodity.
It makes you a sort of Nelson Bunker Hunt of nutrition.
Thin is politically 'correct'.

The bottom line (no pun intended) is that it's pointless
to kick against the traces. Slimming is no longer an
option but the inevitable concomitant of being alive in
the late twentieth century. Like learning to use a word
processor, or send a fax. *Après* Twiggy, we can never 'go
home' again. It is unlikely that our concept of perfect
feminine beauty will soon again repose in nicely rounded,
apron-clad mums, smiling sweetly at sproglettes and
baking apple tarts somewhere in Cumbria or Kansas.

Feminists feel aggrieved as large numbers of women
willingly starve in an effort to conform to exacting
standards of beauty which – it's claimed – are dictated
and imposed by men. But it can also be argued that the
urge to slim is part of the legacy of the feminist move-
ment. Feminism undoubtedly 'raised the game' for
women, transforming perceptions and expectations. We
quickly learned that we could 'have it all' – homes,
families and career success. We could capably handle
corporate mergers and Wednesday school run. We
could control our lives, and our bodies. Slim figures

offset by 'power' shoulder-pads seemed to go with the territory. 'Thin' belonged in the workplace. 'Fat' was cosy, and stayed at home.

We cannot fairly blame men for this breakneck and competitive lifestyle. It is not conspiracy, collusion or plot. We brought it on ourselves. We have become perfectionists. Today's women – sixties generation baby-boomers – do not suffer their own shortcomings gladly. They believe profoundly in the 'perfectibility of the self', and work hard to create a first-class product. Magazines assure us that 'all things are possible'; that there are no limits to our potential achievements. The permanent quest for self-improvement is presented as something we owe to our loved ones, and – more importantly – to ourselves. Perfect slimness is now one of the hallmarks of success; like a Porsche, a seat on the board or an Amex gold card. It tells the world that you've got things buttoned down. Your ducks are in a row. It is an outward sign of savvy, sophistication and good management.

There is little point in constructing elaborate social theories about sexual 'power struggles' to protect our-selves from the inevitable need to diet. What matter if the demand for slimness seems imposed on us from outside ... by men, perhaps, or the fashion industry? The fact is that we have now absorbed the messages, and they are part of us. Try as we may, we cannot turn back the clock. Resist, and we waste valuable years – but find no genuine peace of mind:

FAT-THINK

1. A diet is a form of *submission*. I don't 'sell out'.

2. There's no rule to say that everyone has to be *Thin*!

3. I gotta be 'me'. My plumpness is an expression of my uniqueness as a human being.

4. My partner likes me. The cat is satisfied.

5. I'm very happy with my life. Wouldn't change a thing.

6. Thirty-four. The same age as Michelle Pfeiffer.

7. It's just that my hair's been impossible lately.

If you have never been as slim as you'd like, it is hard to imagine how the quality of life can improve when you've shed even a few unwanted pounds. You *feel* lighter, and more energetic. Your tummy gets smaller, your hips and thighs firmer. Your face takes on a neater, more defined shape. If your diet is balanced, hair and skin texture often improve. Your clothes hang nicely, and feel comfortable instead of pulling. Even your hands and feet get smaller. If you have been very fat, and lose weight, you will breathe more easily, and may also notice that the quality of your voice improves.

THIN-THINK

Consider this: if you spend the same amount of time and energy organizing new eating habits, chances are that you will successfully reduce. Your positive self-image will then rest on a firmer foundation. The fact is that disciplined dieting – hard as it is – is *easier* than spraining your psyche to convince yourself that it isn't necessary. It is easier than coming to terms with a shape you dislike. It is more straightforward than carrying the burden of guilt and emotional baggage that goes with surplus weight.

Most important of all, however, are the *psychological* benefits which a slim figure can bring. You have the satisfaction of knowing that you are healthier and fitter. You gain social confidence, and re-discover your own sense of sex-appeal. Friends, family, strangers and colleagues often perceive you differently, and see you with new eyes. This is not to say that weight loss will make you a 'star' and overnight sensation, or guarantee lasting happiness. It will, however, remove an important obstacle to success. In the final analysis, you simply don't *need* those extra pounds. You're better off without them. To adapt Mae West's immortal line:

'I'VE BEEN THIN . . . AND I'VE BEEN FAT.
AND THIN IS BETTER.'

14

THE TRUTH ABOUT FAT

Things Your Doctor Never Told You –
and Should Have

There's no doubt about it: *diet* is one of life's dark areas. To most people, it's about as opaque as theory of structuralism or quantum physics. Experts can't agree on it – so, really, your guess is as good as mine. Or Jane's, or Rosemary's. Or Dr Scarsdale's. Or Mr Rotation's.

To make matters worse, doctors and nutritionists speak of diet as if it were an exact science: 'if the average person, exercising moderately, takes in fewer than 1,200 units of energy per day, he/she will burn body fat, and lose weight.' (Promises, promises!) They set out rules for healthy eating and effective weight loss, and advise on 'good' foods and 'bad' ones. They always seem so *sure*. But, in recent years, it's fair to say that medical opinion has undergone more changes than Madonna's underwear.

Without doubt, public confidence has been shaken. Only a few years ago, fatties were strongly urged to 'cut out starches – bread and potatoes' for best results. They were told to 'increase protein' – usually in the form of lean meat. Dairy products were perceived as 'healthy', as were eggs . . . provided they weren't fried. Spaghetti was a food to avoid, but cheese was fine. We were warned to cut out sugar, but no one spoke about saturated fats.

As the seventies dawned, scientists performed a deft nutritional U-turn. Bread and potatoes came in from the cold – but minus the butter. The once-banned noodle was rehabilitated, and called 'pasta'. Red meat protein ceased to be a staple of weight-reduction diets. (Reconstructed slimmers switched to chicken or fish, and went to work on an egg – white.) People learned to pronounce 'polyunsaturates', got hot under the collar about the great oat bran controversy, and argued into the night about the virtues of extra-virgin olive oil.

Today, there's a new (and disheartening) twist, as some authorities assert that 'diets don't work' at all. Research shows, they say, that those who lose substantial amounts prove unable to sustain the new weight – and regain surprisingly quickly. Worse still, 'Yo-Yo' dieting results in a build-up of fat cells and slowing of metabolic rate, which makes subsequent weight loss even more difficult. Such findings lend credence to the oft-heard dieters' complaints: 'I've got to starve in order to lose weight' or 'I gain pounds if I so much as *sniff* a Mars bar!'

Difficult, though, to interpret this new piece of medical wisdom. What are doctors trying to tell us? That '*nothing* is possible'? That we should reconcile ourselves to the shapes we were born with? That we shouldn't even *try*? Pathetic, really. A clear admission by the medical profession that they've thrown in the cotton swab, and are powerless to help. Outmanoeuvred by fat cells. Outflanked by flab.

They continue to emphasize the importance of exercise, but are now reluctant – except in cases of extreme obesity – to preach self-denial, in the face of evidence that, for most fatties, long periods of sacrifice produce no lasting reward. The one thing they'll say for sure (if cornered) is that, if you eat *no food at all* for long periods, you'll expire. (Just before the end – with luck – you may make the cover of *Vogue*.)

SPIN DOCTORS

Doctors, in short, have been better at providing 'spin' than 'THIN'. They have had limited success at helping fat people to become slim . . . and stay that way. No wonder we are sceptical.

Admit it, doctors, nutritionists, endocrinologists. You haven't cracked it. There are more things in heaven, earth, mind and metabolism than you can understand, or science can explain . . . like the sheer perversity of the average fat-cell when under threat. So, stand aside, while those of us in the Real World re-examine a few of your pet theories:

Medical Myths about Diet

1. Doctor Says:

'Choose sensible foods, and you can lose weight without hunger.'

Truth:

No chance. You are going to be *very* hungry. (Think Pavarotti on a spa diet.) If you are limiting calorie intake to, say, 1,000 per day for women, and 1,500 for men (or even fewer) – and assuming you lead a relatively 'active' life (if, for example, you get out of bed in the morning) – you are likely to feel *ravenous*. It's best to be prepared, so that you don't surrender at the first pang.

The truth is that 'diet' foods – low in fat, and often with a high water content – simply do *not* sustain you for the same period of time as a 12 ounce sirloin, or a slab of bread and peanut butter. If lunch at 1.00 p.m. consists of a few raw vegetables, a 'portion' of fruit, and a slice of (unbuttered) wholemeal bread, you'll want lunch again by one-thirty. Trust me.

My Tip:

Graze! When on a low-calorie, low-fat diet, this is the best way to keep hunger at bay. The objective is to get yourself through the day with as little discomfort as possible. When your tummy rumbles and will-power flags, buy yourself a few extra hours with – let's say – a glass of tomato juice and an unsalted rice cake at 3.00 p.m. At 5.00 p.m. one plain very low fat yogurt (topped with a few slices of fresh banana) should see you through until dinner at 7.30. Of course, after your (meagre) 400 calorie evening meal (see Chapter 5 for diagram of portion-size), expect to be famished again by bedtime. You know you're on a *serious* diet when you'd happily swap an hour of erotic ecstasy for a bowl of Shreddies with skimmed milk.

2. Doctor says:

'You can eat as much as you like, as long as it's raw carrot.'

Truth:

Don't be taken in by this one. You can *never* eat as much as you like of *anything* – no matter how low in calories or fats. There is a good reason for this. Natural fatties have large capacities, and if you encourage your

---

FAT-THINK

All I've eaten this week is cherries and I'm not losing an ounce, even

appetite to think that the lid is off, 'as much as you like' will turn out to be more than you really need.

But it's only celery? No matter. When your tummy feels full, you're *too comfortable*. Those lazy little fat cells relax, and tend to stick around. If you want them to move, you've got to bludgeon them to death. Weight Watchers can say what they like about never needing to feel hungry while on a diet; I don't believe them. Experience tells me that you've got to suffer to lose weight. Misery lets your fat cells know you mean business.

THIN-THINK

My Tip:

Aim to cut the *amount* of food you eat – all food. In most fatties, mind, appetite and tummies have slipped 'out of sync'. They are seduced by the sheer sensation of eating: the feel, taste and smell. Often, hunger has little to do with it.

Nor are they truly in touch with their own needs. Feeling a bit empty, they begin to eat – but fail to notice the point (usually quite early on) when they've had enough, and are once again comfortable. Instead, they keep on eating until the plate is empty ... or stomachs register 'stuffed'.

A good tip, therefore, is to *concentrate* as you eat. Try to identify the earliest point at which hunger stops. Resolve to stop eating when you are beginning to feel satisfied, but are not 'full'. At first, this feels about as frustrating as coitus interruptus. But, if you push away from the table at this stage, you're likely to find that you've had enough. There is a sort of 'repletion time-lag'. Food just eaten takes a bit of time to 'settle'. So, wait fifteen minutes or so. Then, if you're still genuinely 'hungry', you can always eat more.

For example: the first course to a dinner is often quite filling. It takes the 'edge' off an appetite, and goes a long way towards satisfying needs. Most aspiring skinnies can – if they're honest – comfortably stop eating soon afterwards ... perhaps halfway through the main course. But, if you're enjoying yourself too much – and drinking alcohol as well – you're unlikely to notice. Pleasure and conviviality carry you forward, and concentration slips. Before you know it, you've missed the critical moment.

Therefore, beware the 'momentum' of eating. Beware, too, of your own perception that 'proper' meals consist of *three* courses, and that it's *unnatural* to stop after only one. It isn't. You should. There's some truth to the old adage that the best form of exercise, when dieting, is pushing away from the table ... early. Being in touch with your body – and alert to its needs – is a vital part of THIN-THINK. Don't *eat* so hard that you miss the signals.

FAT-THINK

a. The vegetable soup is so yummy. I can manage seconds.

b. Same goes for the chicken kebabs.

c. Sure, I'm hungry for dessert! I've only had two courses.

THIN-THINK

a. I started with a mixed salad. It was pretty filling.

b. Big hamburger! I don't think I really need the second half.

Another tip: try *toying with food*. Some dieters claim that this is the key to surviving social occasions. They stop eating halfway through a restaurant or family meal, but preserve the illusion of continued participation by toying with what's left on the plate. They cut it up, spread it around, and bury the escalope under the spinach. Fine, if it works for you! But, be warned that toying is rather testing. Many fatties find that they need to push the plate firmly away – or find a new home for the contents. (Skinny but voracious teenaged boys can help here.) Fatties should take care lest 'toying' with food turns into 'picking away at the edges'. Remember that a calorie is a calorie even if it occurs at the very perimeter of a chip.

3. Doctor says:

'Healthy eating gives you extra energy, and a sense of renewed vitality.'

Truth:

After weeks on a strict, low-fat diet which is resulting in weight loss, you'll feel exhausted. Poleaxed. Shattered and blasted. Not to mention draggy and irritable. As blitzed as Roseanne Barr after two hours of high-impact aerobics.

It stands to reason. After all, you're expending the same amount of energy as usual (or more, if you've increased exercise) but providing the body with less fuel. The hope is that it will draw on – and use – its reserves of *fat*. Physically and emotionally, this can be draining. True enough, *physical activity* (running up a flight of stairs) will seem easier once you've shed spare pounds. Meanwhile, you can reasonably expect to feel 11 a.m. droop, 4 p.m. droop, and 10 p.m. droop. Some days, this will extend to twenty-four-hour droop.

Doctors will tell you that 'healthy' foods – in particular, complex carbohydrates – provide a slow but 'steady' source of energy. This allows you to maintain vitality while dieting. Bad eating habits, they warn, ultimately sap energy. The 'sugar rush' you get from your mid-morning Milky Bar feels great, but is soon expended – leaving you with a corresponding 'low'. Desirable diet foods should provide 'even' energy distribution throughout the day.

Fine, in theory. (Though, personally, I never met a sugar rush I didn't like.) It stands to reason that, if your past eating habits have been shameful (a plate of chips and a jam doughnut at lunch, chocolates and prawn crisps at tea, and a take-away bucket of fried chicken for dinner) you may feel a new sense of lightness and well-being. For a bit.

But, for relatively sensible eaters who nevertheless carry a spare tyre or two, low calorie diets can be surprisingly enervating. In female fatties, this is specially evident prior to a menstrual period, when metabolic needs increase. Boy, are you zapped! It's an effort of will to get through the working day. By 4.00 p.m., you're desperate. Craving the old sugar rush, you'd kill for a Kit Kat. Swim in a milk shake. Murder for a Mars Bar. Instead, you take a bite of a long-term, low-level complex carbohydrate . . . a slice of wholemeal bread. Nothing happens. Where's lift-off?

My Tip:

At this critical juncture, a cup of coffee or tea can help. (Drink with skimmed milk, but without sugar. A dash of powdered cinnamon adds interest to sugarless coffee.) If things get *really* bad – or, as your tea-time 'treat' for the day – allow yourself a scant half-teaspoon of sugar . . . just enough to take the bitter 'edge' off the taste of the drink. It's surprising what a 'lift' this small amount can provide. But, sweeten only *one* cup per day in this way . . . and *not* before bedtime.

Also good for instant energy: freshly-squeezed orange juice – or a segmented orange. Either contains moderate amounts of natural sugar, which the body seems to convert easily into instant energy (try it!). If you choose the juice, make sure it's fresh, and contains no added sugar. Natural pulp in the drink is helpful, as it provides some roughage. Again, avoid any orange juice or drink labelled 'made with concentrate' – even if the manufacturer specifies 'no added sugar'. Concentrates can contain substantial amounts of sugar (even without adding any) . . . and no pulp.

Generally speaking, one fresh orange (approximately 50 calories) provides the desired 'lift' with *fewer calories* and more fibre than a medium-sized glass of orange juice. The only drawback is that oranges are a nuisance to peel, and a bit messy for, say, office consumption. What the heck! Orange stains on the Annual Report and Accounts – and fragments of peel under your fingernails – are a small price to pay for a diet-friendly sugar rush.

Desperate? Hands off that Yorkie Bar. P-p-p-put down the Penguin. Instead:

a. Dip a teaspoon (once!) into a jar of *peanut butter*. Don't heap the teaspoon, either. Level it off. Now, eat it . . . and follow with a small glass of ice-cold skimmed milk. OK? That's all you need. You won't feel starved anymore, because peanut butter is a remarkable food. Although it's high in calories and fats, it's a good source of instant energy . . . and h-e-a-v-y, so a little bit goes a long way. Sort of the nutritional equivalent of plutonium. So, no cheating with a second spoonful!

b. P-p-p-pick up a *prune*. Better still: keep a box of California (Sunsweet) seedless prunes in your refrigerator. They'll last forever in their original container, and – if covered – will stay moist. They're sweet – like candy, but also provide useful fibre. Eat no more than one or two a day, since they're relatively high in calories. Prunes go well with that glass of cold skimmed milk . . . or, alternatively, chop one in pieces, and mix with some plain, very low fat natural yogurt. (Loseley's works well.) They provide that satisfying 'lift', but have more to offer than the 'empty' calories in your average chocolate bar. As an added bonus for dieters – prunes keep things moving and your tummy flat.

4. Doctor says:

'Once you've lost weight and learned new eating-habits, your appetite shrinks.'

Truth:

Wanna bet? Once a junkie, always a junkie. Let yourself go, and you're hooked again in no time. Inside Elizabeth

Taylor at 8½ stone lurks the ever-present threat of Elizabeth Taylor at 13 stone – and rising. Breathes there a former fatty (however slim!) who does not fear that, by following natural inclinations, he/she would soon balloon to an obscene size? 'What if,' you think, picking your way abstemiously through the raw cauliflower florets, 'what if I *started* eating . . . and couldn't *stop?*'

It's often implied that a new figure – once achieved – is easy to maintain. Fat chance. (Ask Oprah.) True enough, you now understand the error of your ways; healthy eating means herbal tea and an apple at 4.00 p.m., not a bag of Cheez Twists and a Snickers. But the urge remains, and must be kept in check. Ditto, your appetite. Yes, doctor, my tummy has shrunk two sizes, but I'm here to tell you that its capacity remains as large as ever. I can still out-eat Meatloaf on a hungry day, no problem.

Here's the hideous truth, flab-fighters. The *more* weight you lose, the *harder* it is to lose weight. Experience shows that the metabolism of the born-again skinny slows down. Sluggish? No. More like *stationary*. Soon, you have to fast like Gandhi in order to drop an ounce or two.

The problem is that the bodies of the formerly fat show a lifelong tendency to return to type. Doctors, take note. This is undocumented, of course, but I happen to know that fat cells *think* – and they have long memories. They pine for the good old days when you were a pneumatic teenager, and they had plenty of company.

5. Doctor says:

'Calories are just measurements of units of energy – a calorie is a calorie.'

Truth:

Wrong again! It's clear to me that some calories are *more fattening* than others. It is foolish to assume that they are nutritionally equal or 'neutral'. Some are malevolent. For instance: 100 calories-worth of lettuce and raw veg is 'user-friendly' and won't add flab – but 100 calories-worth of ice cream *will*. If you're following a calorie-controlled diet (1,000 to 1,500 a day) and stick to grilled chicken or fish, and salads dressed with lemon juice, you'll lose weight. Eventually. But, starve all day, then use your precious allowance on beer and a pizza, and see what happens. Fat City, right? My theory is that the more you *enjoy* food, the more fattening it is. Client pleasure excites calories, and the little sods plot and scheme.

My Tip:

Beat them at their own game. Eat only foods which are 'healthy', and bore you to tears. Sheer tedium destroys the potency of calories, and you lose weight.

6. Doctor says:

'Exercise is a dieter's best friend – the key to successful weight loss.'

Truth:

It also makes you very tired while (at the same time) stimulating appetite. Fatties will be aware that, these days, *exercise* gets a better press than Mother Teresa. Doctors get quite exercised about it. They typically recommend four 30-minute sessions of aerobic workout per week, combined with a daily intake of 1,000 to 1,500 calories for effective weight loss. But, mild scepticism is called for.

The theory is that exercise turns fat to muscle, and also – if performed regularly – speeds up metabolic rate, so that dieters burn more calories. Maybe this works for natural athletic skinnies like Zola Budd and Seb Coe, or for aerobics die-hards like Jane Fonda ... but count me out. I accept, of course, that exercise benefits my cardio-vascular system. But, it does not exhilarate me – it makes me very tired. Furthermore, it makes me *ravenous*. I once did thirty lengths of the pool, and emerged hungry enough to eat the lifeguard. Just when he thought it was safe to go back in the water.

This is not to deny the importance of regular physical activity to a healthy lifestyle. (Too often, a fatty's only form of exertion is moving slowly between fixed points: say, from the front door to the car, or the television to the sofa.) I'd merely introduce a note of caution: avoid *stimulating* your appetite if you want to keep it in check. The good news is that, after thirty minutes of strenuous workout, you may be too weak to open the refrigerator door.

My Tip:

Spoil your appetite. There are several ways to do this. Flattened after your designer workout with Jane, Cindy, Callan or Cher? Hit the Evian. Yes, gallons of designer *water* will replenish lost fluids and designer *perspiration*. As a bonus, it helps to create a satisfied 'full' feeling. Expensive water has a way of making you feel you're getting the reward you deserve.

Looking forward to *eating* after exercise? It's a bad idea to approach your next full meal with a yawning chasm where your stomach ought to be. Instead, try a 'spoiler'. Have an apple or piece of fresh fruit to go with your mineral water. Also, perhaps, a salt-free rice cake (25 to 30 calories) or an (unbuttered) slice of wholemeal bread from your daily allowance. This will help to 'bulk out' the water, deceive your stomach, and create a more comfortable feeling. Wait at least half an hour before eating your next meal. The 'spoiler' will have taken the edge off your appetite, allowing you to eat more moderately. (Something short of cramming food into your mouth with both hands.)

7. Doctor says:

'Snacking is bad. Dieters should eat three "square" meals a day, and avoid "picking" in between.'

Truth:

Snacking – or 'grazing' – can often *help* dieters. There's a school of thought which suggests that it's preferable to eat 'little and often' when trying to lose weight. It's already been said that many low-fat or 'diet' foods quickly 'disappear', leaving you hungry. Unable to last hours until your next full meal, you naturally reach for the nearest tube of Pringles.

Don't. Instead, eat *when you're hungry* . . . but rely on low-cal snackettes. Raw fruit and vegetables, cauliflower and broccoli florets, unsalted rice cakes, tomato juice, very low fat plain yogurt, and the odd Tupperware container of fresh pineapple are all good. California's well-known Pritikin Institute encourages dieters to follow a 'grazing' pattern, providing them with twenty-four-hour access to a trolley of hot jacket potatoes. No salt, no butter or cheese – *certainly* no sour cream – but you can sprinkle with fresh herbs, and eat the skins. (Occasionally, staff find teeth-marks on the trolley.)

Those experts who subscribe to the 'little and often' school of dieting claim that the body is able to process small but continuous amounts of low-fat food more efficiently than occasional hunks. In this way, they say, calories are burnt most effectively. It's a similar principle to maintaining an 'even' heat in the furnace by stoking it frequently, and avoiding starts and stops.

Feel free, therefore, to follow the method which works best for you. Eating *between* meals is fine, provided the day's total calorie intake does not thereby increase. In other words: spread your calories in any way you like . . . but no cheating. Remember that 'grazing' is a way of dealing with hunger – not of squeezing in extra food. (As ever, check that you're genuinely *hungry* before popping so much as a carrot curl into your mouth. There's no point in taking in calories just to pass the time.)

My Tip:

Chances are that, if you're following a fairly rigorous low-fat diet, you'll *need* to eat often. Frequent hunger is a clear sign that things are working. In this sense, the discomfort should be welcomed. But, it can be a nuisance ... especially if you're unprepared. When you're *very* hungry, you're at the mercy of your own needs; desperate to eat, unwilling to wait even the time it takes to peel a stalk of celery. One good thing about a Kit Kat; it doesn't have to be *cleaned*.

Moral: have appropriate snacks *at the ready*. Fill a few Tupperware containers full of fresh pineapple or melon, already cut in convenient bite-sized chunks. Instant gratification, no waiting necessary! Do the same with your raw vegetables. Stock in plain, very low fat yogurts, and a good supply of the other tasteless crunge (rice cakes, melba toast, etc.) essential to a successful diet. *Do not buy* fattening snacks on the grounds that 'it's just for the kids' or 'I'll keep it as a special treat'. In your weakened condition, it's too hard to resist temptation. When the fridge door opens, you want to see only 'safe' diet foods. Don't expect to survive a power struggle with a Toblerone.

PORTABLE FOOD

Most important: when dieting, *always carry food supplies with you!* Otherwise (sooner or later), overwhelming hunger will catch you short, and force you to buy a Cadbury's Crunchie or risk passing out. If this happens, expect no sympathy. You brought it on yourself. Deep down inside, you probably *meant* to engineer a crisis which made it imperative for you to eat a diet-buster.

REMEMBER:
Breaking a diet is a decision . . .
not an 'accident'

To avoid temptation, take preventative action. Never move without supplies of low-calorie 'desperation' food. Practicality suggests that this means *bread* products. (Carrot sticks and fruit are OK but can wilt or ooze in handbag or briefcase.) Take a small plastic bag containing slices of bread, a roll, low-fat crackers or toast . . . all unbuttered, of course, and wholemeal for preference. And – here's the important bit – try to make sure that your rations are *at least a day old*, and semi-stale. That way, you know you'll eat them in emergencies only, since any form of enjoyment is out of the question. (Determined skinnies soon come to appreciate the attractions of antique food.)

8. Doctor says:

'You can continue to *enjoy* food, and still lose weight.'

Truth:

If you're enjoying it, you probably shouldn't be eating it. Although, of course, it depends on what the doctor means by 'enjoy'. Medical men and women have a lot to answer for, here. By raising unrealistic expectations about 'painless' dieting, you can argue that they pre-programme fatties for failure.

Whatever your personal tastes, one thing is sure: you are simply *not* going to 'enjoy' your container of plain, very low fat skimmed milk yogurt as much as, say, the average Dove Bar. The contest between an unsalted rye crisp and a bacon sandwich is no contest. Later (*much* later), you will of course enjoy looking slimmer and feeling fitter. But, do not imagine that 'getting there' is half the fun. To slim successfully, you must reprogramme your mind and expectations. THIN-THINK means setting aside short-term pleasure, and learning to think long-term.

My Tip:

Defer pleasure. Put it off. Postpone and transfer it. Make no mistake; former fatties will miss bad old habits. It's hell to wean yourself away from the level of food enjoyment you have come to expect. It is even more futile (and disappointing) to pretend that low-cal eating delivers the same 'kick' ... that you won't crave your old favourites, or notice the difference. You will, of course. Worse still, you cannot look forward to returning – ever again – to former habits. If you sincerely wish to *become* slim and *stay* slim, you'll have to come to terms with 'pleasure transfer'.

It's a simple trade-off. Goodbye, FAT-THINK, hello, THIN-THINK. You forgo the short-term pleasure of biting into a Midnight Mint – or an After Eight straight from the fridge – for the more *lasting* satisfaction of slipping effortlessly into a size 10 dress. Or zipping up trousers with a small waist and pleated fronts, to find that they're *comfy*. (When you sit, they no longer cut at the crotch. The 'fall' of the pleats is not distorted by your protruding tum.) That's a moment worth a dozen Wall's Cornettos.

9. Doctor says:

'Don't jump on a scale every day. Once a week is enough.'

Truth:

Weigh yourself *every* day, at the same time of day. Preferably in the morning, before eating or getting dressed. There are good reasons for this. First – when you're on a strict diet – the scale is hard to resist, and can provide important incentive. Second, it's the only

accurate way to monitor progress. (The argument against it is that diets are often slow to take effect. Fatties risk losing heart when they can't see daily 'results' – which could well appear by the end of the week.)

Fair enough. But, daily weigh-ins have another purpose. They serve as a check that you're not actually *gaining* weight. Remember that dieting takes practice before you get it right. It is not unusual to find that – in trying to eat more low-fat foods – new dieters inadvertently eat *more*. In women especially, a misjudged change in habits can lead to immediate gain, particularly at the 'wrong' time of month. Four extra pounds in a single week is not unusual. Best to nip any problem in the bud, before it gets out of hand. Even experienced slimmers must be assured that they're moving at the right speed in the right direction. Fatties need frequent checks on their balances.

10. Doctor says:

'If you stop worrying about "diets", and concentrate on healthy eating – your weight will take care of itself.'

Truth:

Dream on, doc. This is the myth of *'self-regulation'* – perhaps the cruellest one of all. It implies many questionable (and soul-destroying) things all at once, such as:

a. The discipline of cutting calories and fats is a waste of time – self-indulgent and neurotic.

b. Your obsession with diet distorts the 'natural' balance between food intake and correct body weight. Weight would stabilize at an appropriate level if you'd simply eat normally, and get out of your own way.

NOTE to medical practitioners:
Fatties are no longer *capable* of eating 'normally'. They have lost track of what 'normal' *is*.

c. There is – for each individual – a 'natural' weight . . . a level at which body weight (unless manipulated) will automatically stabilize.

Note:

Some doctors subscribe to the notion that there is a natural 'set point' – an *optimum weight* which varies for each person, and which the body strives to maintain. According to this theory, a cut in calories prompts the body to respond by slowing metabolic rate . . . thus reverting to 'set point' – and thwarting dieters.

There is, as yet, no proof that such a 'set point' exists. (Most experts think it unlikely.) If it *does* exist, it's still *less* likely that wannabe skinnies will be content with it.

Other 'Self-Regulation' Myths Which Fatties Should Ignore:

a. When you're young, you can eat what you want without gaining weight.

b. When you're old, you can eat what you want without gaining weight.

MYTH EXPLODED

The achievement (and maintenance) of a genuinely slim figure is not – for the vast majority of us – an accident. It does not 'come naturally'. It requires determination, and sustained effort. It's unfair to suggest that – were we not weak and vain creatures, who abuse food and 'subvert' our systems – we would not be fat. It seems that, in the eyes of the medical profession, fatties are in a 'no win' situation. They *become* fat because they eat too much. They *remain* fat because they try to diet.

It's understood, doc, that you're conscious of the dangers of obsessive dieting. You prefer to emphasize *healthy eating* – which helps to achieve weight loss, and has a more 'positive' feel to it than the deprivation normally associated with *diet*. But, make no mistake! Slimmers need a bit of *both* to feel good in Lycra. We all know that the range of 'normal' in most height-weight charts is wide. Few aspiring skinnies are genuinely happy at the top end.

Here is a simple observation which – once and for all – explodes the *myth of self-regulation*:

FAT FACT ONE:
It Takes Two or Three Weeks of Strict Dieting to Lose One Pound.

FAT FACT TWO:
It Takes an Hour of Steady Bingeing to Gain Six.

In fact (as all fatties know), it is frighteningly easy to gain several pounds *overnight* if you:

     a. go out to dinner (2 pound gain)

     b. get a period (2 to 3 pound gain)

     c. go out to dinner, and get a period (3 pound gain)

     d. go out to dinner, *enjoy* it, and get a period (4 pound gain).

11. Doctor says:

'If you're gaining weight, you're eating too much. You can't get fat by just *looking* at food.'

Truth:

Sez who? Fatties know better! For instance: try dieting all day – then stare at a slice of cream cake left over in the fridge, or at the pastry tray in a restaurant. Your mouth begins to water, right? It's just possible that, at this point, a hitherto undocumented bio-chemical change takes place. Your whole body begins to *anticipate calorie intake*. Enzymes are activated. The endocrine system moves to 'red alert'. Moribund fat cells – shaken from a diet-induced stupor – spring to life. 'Hang in there,' they shout to each other. 'She's considering a cream cake!' Fat cells are ever hopeful. They know it ain't over till the fat lady sings. And she has to *stop eating* first.

All this explains why *just looking* at food makes you feel fatter. It stimulates the desire to eat . . . which seems to generate body heat. You have aroused your entire metabolic system. In anticipation of food, your stomach expands. Waistbands strain. The scale creeps relentlessly upwards. Or is it a fatty's fevered imagination?

My Tip:

If it's fattening, *don't eat it*. Don't even *think* about eating it.

12. One final myth

There is a twelfth *myth* – not promulgated by doctors, but more a fond hope expressed by fatties themselves:

THE DIETER'S IMPOSSIBLE DREAM
I'll diet until I'm 5 pounds below my ideal weight.
Then I'll enjoy the blissful experience of gaining 5 pounds WITHOUT GUILT!

Through long weeks, months or years of self-imposed restraint, this is the fantasy which keeps many fatties going. The moment of delicious abandon. The day when the lid comes off. The opportunity to know – for a nutritional nano-second – the pure pleasure of carefree eating.

Truth:

Sorry, fatties. Gastronomically speaking, you can never go home again. Never relive the youthful delights of guilt-free Liquorice Allsorts and Cadbury's Creme Eggs. Or take-away burgers and chocolate shakes. Or birthday cakes smothered in brightly-coloured hundreds-and-thousands. Not that you can never *eat* these things again. It's just that you can never eat them again with a *free mind*. Having mastered the art (and mind-set) of effective weight control, you're stuck with it. It's part of growing up. THIN-THINK is a sort of nutritional 'loss of innocence'.

Anyway, it would take more than 5 pounds of leeway to allow you to genuinely *eat without guilt*. It would require nothing short of a miracle. Only a sense of *cosmic destiny* (or similar) could provide the justification you'd need. Captain Kirk would have to land the Starship Enterprise in your back garden, and walk slowly towards you, saying:

> **'MRS SIMPKINS, YOU CAN SAVE THE WORLD. BUT IT WILL REQUIRE GREAT SACRIFICE. YOU WILL HAVE TO EAT A HÄAGEN-DAZS MOCHA CHIP ALMOND SUNDAE WITH HOT FUDGE IN A WAFFLE CONE. DO IT, MRS SIMPKINS. DO IT FOR THE GOOD OF THE GALAXY.'**

The point is that it takes a sense of *intergalactic mission* to provide natural fatties with a guilt-free eating experience.

Actually, even if you *were* 5 pounds below your target weight, you wouldn't dare let yourself go. **Here's why:**

1. You'd decide you *liked* yourself at that weight.

2. You'd be afraid that, if you 'relaxed control', you'd gain it all back.

3. By the time you'd dieted to a point 5 lbs. below your target weight, you'd be eating next-to-nothing anyway. Your metabolism would have slowed to a virtual stop. You wouldn't need to

binge to gain 5 lbs. You could just drink a glass of water.

15

EXCUSES, EXCUSES:

Shedding the Psychology Which Keeps You Fat

When it comes to diet, doctors have no monopoly on clichés and cant. There are lots of little lies which we fatties like to tell *ourselves*. A prime example of FAT-THINK, they let us off the hook when we fail to lose weight. Worse still, they provide reasons not to *try*. Recognize these?

1. Losing Weight is Impossible For Me – I'm a 'Special Case'

'Diets don't *work* for me!' protests the defeated slimmer. 'I'm a freak ... the exception to every rule.' You've heard it – perhaps said it – a thousand times. 'I have to *starve* to lose weight'; 'If I eat "normally", I gain pounds'; 'I get hungrier than thin people'; 'I'm naturally inclined to be heavy.'

NO EXCUSES

Nice try, but the hard truth is that DIETING IS HELL FOR EVERYONE. *Everyone* has to starve in order to lose even a few ounces. Fat is the stubbornest stuff since Saddam

Hussein, and you can't get rid of it unless you attack it for extended periods.

Prepare for what you may not wish to hear. Unless you've a thyroid abnormality (you probably don't, but you may almost wish you did!) you *can* lose weight. If you're in any doubt, look at Third World famine victims. True starvation works every time.

Of course, everyone's metabolism is different. But, not *that* different. It is highly doubtful that anyone – including you – can become (or remain) fat on a thousand calories a day. A *genuine* thousand calories a day. Counting everything.

P.S. Just for the record: 1,000 calories a day is really a very small amount of food. Many people routinely consume nearly that number at breakfast alone! A medium-sized glass of orange juice can run to 100 calories. A small container of low-fat, fruit-flavoured yogurt is worth about 150 calories. That's a quarter of your total diet allowance for the day. (Imagine what happens if you add eggs, toast and bacon.)

2. My Metabolism is Abnormally Slow

Again, probably not. There are huge gaps in medical understanding about the workings of metabolic rate, but the plain fact is that it takes very little food to keep a person alive and healthy. Most of us are used to packing away far more than we really need. We believe we require (and should be able to process) three 'squares' a day.

It seems that our perceptions about food have failed to keep up with changing times. Years ago, when life was harder, we probably *needed* to eat more. Today, few women do heavy manual work or farming. Shopping takes place in covered malls. Homes are centrally heated, everyone rides to work, and spends lots of time sitting down facing computers or tellies. It's a good bet that the metabolic rate of the *entire population* is slowing down. We all need lighter, healthier diets. But old habits die hard, and our perceptions of 'normal' intake date from the turn of the last century. Whatever granny said, we just don't need that much food anymore. We may *want* it – even be hungry for it ... but it is no sin against nutrition to skip a cooked breakfast.

Take the average nineties kid. How much physical energy does he expend while:

  a. being transported to school in a Toyota Previa

  b. mastering Super Mario Brothers on his personal Game Boy

  c. inflating a new pair of 'pump action' Nike Airs.

Experienced dieters will be aware that standard 'energy expenditure' charts are now hopelessly out of date. Most measure the number of calories used while performing energetic tasks that we seldom – if ever – do: i.e., shovelling snow, painting the house, washing the car, scrubbing floors or hanging out laundry. Today, more relevant *contemporary* information is needed. *Did you know*, for example, that you can burn up to 20 calories every fifteen minutes by (vigorously) trying on clothes in a fitting room? (Probably more in a *communal* chang-ing room, since you have to fight for a mirror.) You use

15 calories in fifteen minutes while pounding an electric typewriter (probably only 12 calories over the same period on a word processor – even allowing for the extra task of loading the sheet-feeder.)

In short, it's rare that dieters can blame slow or sluggish metabolic rates for failure to lose weight. It's just that modern life – stressful as it is – demands little *physical* effort. We suffer plenty of anxiety, but use surprisingly few calories. Run through a list of routine daily tasks, and the problems are clear. For example,

Can you estimate the calorie-burn rate of each of the following activities:

  a. micro-waving popcorn

  b. having a blow-dry

  c. lifting a credit-card from your wallet, and presenting it to a sales assistant

  d. pressing the 'last number recall' button on your touch-tone phone

  e. ordering in pizza

  f. using the short codes on your fax machine

  g. inserting a satellite television de-scrambler card into the appropriate slot.

*Estimated calorie-burn rate
over a fifteen-minute period:*

approximately 2 calories per activity.

3. I'm Not Fat – I'm Big-Boned

Nice try, but there's a limit to how much 'bigger' your bones can be than other people's. They can be *longer* – which will probably make you a tall person. They may be a bit 'thicker' – but probably not much, or you'd look awfully peculiar for your gender (like Arnold Schwarzenegger in a dress). You can have a 'broad frame' – but, again, that's hardly the point. Even large frames, square shoulders or child-bearing hips can carry *too much fat*. Sorry. Chances are that skeletal structure is not your problem. Padding is.

Tennis star Martina Navratilova can fairly be called 'big boned' – but she's far from fat. Further weight loss would not transform her into a tiny slip of a thing. She was not cut out to be Tinkerbell. Nevertheless, she has a slim, muscular appearance. Whatever your individual build, the story's the same. You can be that way and THIN, or that way and FAT.

4. Fat Runs in My Family . . . It's 'Coded in the Genes'

'Genes', as a wise endocrinologist once said, 'are not destiny.' This deserves some thought. Each of us is born with a genetic 'blueprint' – and we spend the rest of our lives working on it. Refining and improving it. Developing the raw material. *Transforming* it if necessary. Provided you are healthy, you are *not* the helpless victim of your own chromosomes.

We've become quite adept at manipulating *some* characteristics. Many a natural brunette becomes a convincing blonde or redhead. Clever contact lenses make brown eyes blue. Exercise tones congenital flab, plastic surgeons make large noses small, and orthodontists straighten crooked teeth. If there *is* an inherited predisposition to be 'fat' (and expert opinion is divided on this point) we can choose to change behaviour and fix that, too.

It appears, however, that many people cope with the *temporary* trauma of plastic surgery (or orthodonture) more easily than the *permanent* discomfort of restricted eating. In their minds, pain is tolerable if it's finite ... but diets go on and on. It is impossible to look forward to a day when the diet will be 'over', and the goal achieved . . . when they can return to what they perceive as 'normal', comfortable eating.

As fatties know too well, DIETS ARE NEVER OVER. For those who wish to stay slim, 'hunger management' becomes a permanent way of life. This is, of course, a daunting thought . . . but successful skinnies find ways to adapt. If there's a secret to THIN-THINK, it's learning the knack of simulating the physical and emotional satisfaction of a 'full' stomach on an intake of far fewer calories.

Meanwhile, the 'nature vs. nurture' debate continues, raising tantalizing questions. Are we fat because our parents are fat? *How* is fatness inherited – if, indeed, it is? Do we simply follow our parents' poor habits, eating excessive amounts of the wrong foods? Is there, perhaps, a genetic tendency to exercise too little . . . or a predisposition towards 'sluggish' metabolic rate? So far, answers are not clear.

In the end, does it matter? Whether you're *born* fat, *achieve* fatness or have it *thrust* upon you (too many meals in the office canteen?) the remedy is the same. DIET.

When you come from a long line of hefties, it's easy to believe that your suffering is specially acute because you're flying in the face of genetic destiny. Nature, you reflect, never *intended* you to be thin. But, remember that DIETING IS HELL for everyone! Rest assured that, in a normal, healthy person, there is no 'inborn' impediment to weight loss . . . that 'genes are not destiny'. You *can* succeed. If you are to achieve an enviably slim figure, however, the need to diet is unavoidable. It's coded in the jeans.

5. I Can't Afford to Diet

You're out of date. This was a *really good excuse* when we all thought that successful weight loss required 'a-sirloin-a-day'. Now, we know better. Or think we do. Whatever virtues bread, bran, fruit and vegetable fibre may lack – they are, on the whole, relatively cheap.

Breathes there a fatty with income so low, that he can't afford the occasional plate of pasta? Complex carbohydrates are – generally speaking – more affordable than meat, processed foods, biscuits or cakes. Fresh vegetables can be grown in small gardens or (if you don't set your heart on a record-sized marrow) even in window boxes.

True, *fruit* is sometimes expensive (like peaches, nectarines and strawberries) but other staples – apples, pears and oranges – aren't bad. What's *really* expensive is high fat 'convenience' food. Steer forever clear of any product which calls itself: ham roll, pork pie, pre-sliced 'luncheon meat' (vacuum-packed pink slices) or 'turkey loaf'. They contain small quantities of real food, bulked out with fillers, and pressed into artificial shapes. (Turkey was never meant to have *corners*.) They cost a lot, since you're paying for packaging and partial preparation. Worst of all – you're purchasing *fat*!

Claiming that diets are 'too expensive' is classic FAT-THINK. Freely translated, it means:

a. I don't really *want* to diet. (Bring on the pressed ham!)

b. I like the taste of junk food. (Bring on the spam!)

c. I can't bear the hassle of preparing 'raw' food. (Bring on the rectangular turkey!)

Fatties who plead financial constraint may also be exhibiting signs of 'VEGA-PHOBIA'. Fear of broccoli.

6. I Don't Have Time to Diet

This is, perhaps, the wimpiest excuse of all. What does it mean, anyway? That preparation of 'diet' food takes longer? (It doesn't. It's as easy to cook pasta as pork chops.) That it's 'different' from ordinary family eating, and somehow involves doubling up? (It needn't be. See Chapter 9, 'Fat and Families'.) That it's 'exotic' food, and difficult to obtain, or 'complicated' food which can't be eaten on the run? Gimme a break! We're talking about bread and fruit.

Maybe what's meant is, 'I don't have time to *exercise*.' This is a bit more convincing, since regular exercise must indeed be 'programmed' into a busy day. But, a change in eating habits should not have scheduling implications. Unless you mean, 'my life only works if I can grab a Milky Way, and keep going.' Here's a tip: grab an apple.

7. I Don't Need to Diet. My Husband/Wife/ Partner Likes Me as I am

If a partner claims to prefer you FAT – or, at any rate, fat-ish – there are several possible explanations:

   a. You're kidding yourself.

   b. He/she is being kind, and sparing your feelings.

   c. Your partner is overweight him or herself, and therefore tolerant of *you*.

   d. Your partner is overweight, and afraid that if *you* slim down, he/she will be under pressure to follow.

   e. Your partner is overweight, and fears that, if you become *slim and desirable*, you'll lose interest in him/her.

f. He/she knows very well that to suggest a diet is to invite *big trouble*.

Male partners are particularly cowardly. A husband or boyfriend can usually be counted upon to insist that you're 'thin enough'. Perhaps he *means* it. Perhaps he's being loyal, and responding to your clear need for reassurance. Or will simply say anything for a quiet life.

It's also conceivable that:

a. He's wrong.

b. He's one of a small number of men who are aroused only by overweight women. If so, consider the possibility that he's *weird*.

c. If he loves you 'just as you are', he'll like you *even better* when you've lost some weight.

If in doubt, here's the final test. Ask yourself this question: if Kim Basinger/Michelle Pfeiffer/Claudia Schiffer were to request a date with him, would he back away, protesting, 'Hell, no! She's too *thin*!'

Which women does he fantasize about? Drool over? On telly or in the movies? *Thin* ones, right?

Partners, of course, stand to benefit if you shed surplus weight. However satisfactory your sex life now is, *it will improve* when you feel slim and desirable. Pride and confidence in your body are liberating in bed. But, this is not the main point. Remember:

WHAT YOUR PARTNER/MOTHER/CHILDREN/ BOSS OR HAMSTER THINK IS ULTIMATELY UNIMPORTANT. ONLY <u>YOUR</u> OPINION COUNTS.

AND, CHANCES ARE THAT <u>YOU</u> THINK YOU'RE TOO FAT.

All the loving reassurance in the world won't change that, or deliver true peace of mind, until you take matters in hand. If you *don't* take action:

    a. You will neurotically demand more and more reassurance from partners. (This will fail to set your mind at rest.)

    b. Eventually, your long-suffering partner will lose patience, and leave.

    c. Then you'll have to *diet anyway*, in order to attract a *new* one.

When you look at it this way, dieting seems by far the softest option.

8. Dieting Makes Me Feel Sick

Depends on how you do it ... and on how proficient you become at managing your own eating habits. 'Little and often' – once you've mastered the technique – will see you smoothly and safely through most days. If you plan to break temporarily with your usual routine, be prepared to remain flexible, and adapt things slightly. For example, don't expect to retain a vice-like grip on the day's menu if you're:

    a. Rising at dawn for a flight to Kabul.

    b. Sitting A-levels.

   c. Moving house.

   d. Swimming the Channel.

   e. Meeting his parents for the very first time.

   f. Coming down with 'flu.

If you feel your tummy rumbling, and a headache coming on, for heaven's sake, *eat*. Just try not to choose a chocolate bar.

If you break your diet on a 'hungry' day by downing a Danish or scoffing a sandwich, there's no need to fly your personal flag at half-mast. A 'lapse' is no tragedy, and will set you back little if at all. The following day, you'll be well-placed to pick up the pieces, and start again. *Starting over* is something which all serious dieters must learn to do. (Many times, if necessary.) Do remain resilient. THIN-THINK is the ability to survive occasional set-backs, reject the possibility of defeat – and *carry on*.

Just as vital is the art of 'damage limitation'. Even when caught in the grip of a binge, try to retain *some measure* of control. Most fatties can more easily recover from a minor nutritional mishap than a full-scale disaster (like a bucket o' fried chicken and side order of spare ribs, washed down with a strawberry shake, followed by Christmas pudding 'n' cream). Before you know it, you're drinking Ribena *neat*, and spreading butter on an aspirin. It's too, too disheartening to reflect upon weeks of hard work, undone in twenty minutes of abandon.

That's why diets self-destruct, and people give up in despair. Oh, well, they reason. 'I've ruined it, now. All that wasted effort. I can't possibly go through *more*

weeks of misery, just to arrive back at the same point!'
So, do yourself a favour; avoid a major pig-out. Starting
over is so much easier when you've only slipped a *little*.
Lurching from 'boom' to 'bust' – starvation to blow-out
– is enough to make anyone nauseous.

People who complain of 'feeling sick' on diets are often
plain *hungry*. A frequent 'empty' feeling – until you
learn to handle it – can be unsettling. Others find that
complex carbohydrates – to which they're unaccus-
tomed – sit heavily on their stomachs. Fibre and roughage may initially cause flatulence. In short, filling your
personal void with bran products, raw fruit and vegetables, plain rice and yogurt, when you're used to the
user-friendly, 'easy-melt' feel of egg 'n' chips or processed
cheese slices takes some practice.

Allow for a period of adjustment. Draw encouragement
from the improvement you'll detect in 'regularity' (efficient elimination is, after all, a factor in successful
weight loss!) Rest assured that you are doing your body
a *favour*. Someday – when it recovers from nutritional
shell-shock – it will thank you. The day will come when
you will feel queasy at the mere *sight* of a tea-time fry-
up or a pint of full-cream milk. Strange, but true.

9. I Can't Diet. I Have Too Many Social/ Business Obligations

Unless your boss has served notice that your next promo-
tion is contingent upon remaining *fat*, this one won't
wash.

No 'special pleading'. *Everyone* has obligations. To satisfy Auntie Ethel, you have to eat her famous fudge cake. (Both slices.) An important client loves slap-up lunches, and insists on company. The kids want dinner at McDonalds, and the only item low in cholesterol is the polystyrene box. Your dinner party hostess prepares four courses in Tunbridge, when you'd prefer an evening at home, with soup, salad, and *EastEnders* on telly. Such is life. If these are reasons for not dieting there's no hope for any of us.

As a general rule of thumb, it is nearly *always* possible to eat your way around 'taboo' items. If this proves difficult, you can at least keep portions small. The idea is to 'contain the damage', and live to fight another day. If you are hosting a business or social event, make sure it takes place on *your* terms. Menus – at home or in restaurants – must reflect *your* needs. Guests needn't (and won't) even be aware. Who'd complain, for example, about poached salmon or grilled breast of chicken (remove the skin from your own portion), melon with Parma ham (*you* can discreetly ditch the ham) or spaghetti with fresh tomato sauce and basil?

Do consider – while dieting seriously, and making a major effort to reach your 'target' weight – avoiding *formal* dinner parties. As a guest, you are expected to do your duty by flattering the host and hostess. This generally means accepting the proffered 'seconds' of boeuf Wellington à la crème, or roast duck stuffed with oyster and liver pâté. You undermine your own diet in the interests of people you hardly know, may not care for . . . and will probably never see again.

Instead, enjoy evenings with close friends or family, where you can comfortably 'call the shots': i.e., 'Wendy, I'm going to "pass" on your fab *crème brûlée*. This hurts me more than it hurts you.'

In my view, 'social eating' events for dieters are best held in one of two places:

    a. at the *dieter's* home

    b. in restaurants.

The first choice puts you in control – but may make you feel compelled to offer a few 'fattening' options for guests ... which may, in turn, tempt *you*. (If you concoct a sherry trifle for them, will you really content yourself with a fresh peach?)

Even better – where possible – is to meet and eat in *restaurants*. Both you and your friends can chose what you like. Portion size will be limited, and no one will offer 'seconds'. If your guest chooses a sweet, you can keep company with a chic cappuccino. You can order a bottle of wine, nurse a small glass yourself, and leave the rest to companions. Everyone gets what they want, and *you* get the bill. Never mind. It's a small price to pay for staying *thin*.

One last point: many dieters feel embarrassed and guilty in restaurants. They fear that, since they're not *eating* – they're not *spending* enough. They feel obliged to order more than they really want, so that waiters won't feel 'annoyed'. They are specially worried if others in the party are dieting and therefore not eating much.

Do not, for heaven's sake, fall into this trap. Order only what you want. Restaurants are a *service* industry. They are there to make your life easier. While dieting, it is worth becoming a 'regular' at one or two congenial establishments. Staff grow used to your funny little ways, and know what to expect. You'll find that they are perfectly happy to see you and your guests eat 'little' . . . as long as it's 'often'.

10. My Friends Say I Don't Need to Diet

Maybe they're right. Maybe they're wrong. Maybe they're nice, maybe they're nasty. One thing's for sure.

They're *irrelevant*. Only *you* can be the final judge of whether *you* need to diet. Friends may reassure, deny, support or insist ... but you're the one who must feel 'at home' in your own body. If you've heard their protests, but still feel uneasy about your weight, your choice is clear. **Go for it**.

16
DIET SHORTHAND
The Colour of Calories

The question of what to eat – and what *not* to eat – can confuse even experienced dieters. A calorie-count is just one part of the equation. Wannabe skinnies must also learn to compose 'balanced' meals, to recognize and avoid fats, and to spot potential 'diet-busters' (like a handful of dry roasted peanuts). They should become familiar with different food groups, and how these are metabolized. With practice, many develop a nutritional 'sixth sense'. Call it gut instinct, or *fatties' radar*. A dieter's most valuable tool, its purpose is to detect hidden dangers.

FOOD WITH 'ATTITUDE'

The point is that certain foods possess an 'aura'. They may look innocent enough, and even be low in calories – but they exude *'fat attitude'*. (Food, in expert hands, can be interpreted.)

Take, for example, a platter of steamed or broiled jumbo Gulf shrimp, fresh crab or scampi. They look all right (they're fish, aren't they?) No reason – on the surface of things – why they should not be enjoyed as part of a calorie-controlled diet. But, some nameless dieter's instinct holds you back. The plate of crustaceans is giving off the wrong 'vibes'. Later, it's confirmed that certain varieties of shellfish are, indeed, deceptively high in cholesterol . . . though not necessarily in *calories*.

One give-away is the way the stuff *looks*. Delicious. You can tell at a glance that, if you ate it, you'd *enjoy* it. Enjoyment – as every fatty knows – is fattening. Remember that there is no such thing as 'painless' weight loss. That's why serious dieters will give the shrimp a 'miss' in favour of something devoid of excitement . . . like shredded carrot and raw vegetable salad. Or (equally charmless) clear broth. Stop. Think. Feel the 'aura'. You can sense that shredded carrot has no 'attitude'.

Consommé emits no 'vibes'. Your dieter's radar picks up no signals. It is *safe to proceed*.

THE COLOUR OF CALORIES

Colour is also a good clue. Look for boring, insipid colour if you want to find diet-friendly nutrition. Watery *non-colours* often signify acceptable low-fat, high-fibre, low-calorie dishes. (Think of the grey-beige hue of cooked oat bran. Or steamed cabbage. Or skimmed milk.)

In fact, when a food looks too attractive in any way – beware. Think of the eye-appeal of a deep, rich slice of moist dark chocolate fudge cake . . . the swirl of real cream in coffee . . . or the glossy yellow of freshly scrambled eggs. No doubt about it – calories are *pretty*. They know how to vamp it up, and make the most of themselves. And they really know how to hurt a guy.

So, when dieting, do be guided by available lists of appropriate food choices . . . but, trust your *instincts* as well. You'll soon get the hang of it. Meanwhile – for what it's worth – here is a shorthand (and completely personal) colour-coded diet plan:

1. APPROACH WHITE FOODS WITH CAUTION

Some are dieters' delights: skimmed milk, low-fat cottage cheese, skinless breast of chicken, grilled white fish, raw cauliflower, plain very low fat yogurt . . . even dry white wine (lower in calories than some reds). Others are Fat City: white sugar, cream, ice cream.

2. BROWN FOODS ARE GOOD IF THEY'RE GRAINS, PULSES OR WHOLEMEAL – SKIP THE CHOCOLATE FUDGE CAKE

Brown bread, bran cereals, wholemeal pasta, lentils, pulses and high-fibre foods are the right stuff for dieters. They provide bulk, roughage, and keep you regular. When slimming it's important to feel that you're losing *something* every day.

Beware of *attractive* brown food – especially if it's:

 a. labelled Cadbury's **or**
 b. served in a gravy boat

3. GREEN FOOD IS A DIETER'S BEST FRIEND

Most green things are good: lettuce, green vegetables, melon and fruit. Avoid avocados (not as low cal as their colour implies). Do not dip green foods in lots of runny yellow food (melted butter, hollandaise sauce).

4. CUT DOWN ON RED FOOD – EXCEPT APPLES AND TOMATOES

Red meat can be high in animal fats, and – if you eat it every day – cuts the momentum of your weight loss. Eat sparingly, and cook to a pale shade of diet friendly taupe or brown ... so that much of the fat runs off. You'll know it's right when you hate the way it looks.

As for other red foods: cherries are relatively fattening for fruit – even fresh ones. Strawbs are OK, but skip the cream.

5. ELIMINATE PINK FOOD

Pork products, sausage, bacon, gammon. They're so high in fats, they'll undo your good work. Why bother to suffer if you're going to sabotage your own efforts? Most ham, sausage and bacon also contain nitrates and other preservatives – which, in large doses, kill rodents . . . and don't do *you* much good, either.

6. O.D. ON FRUIT

Pineapple's a good choice; low in calories. Virtually everything else is fine, but, be careful with bananas, which only pretend to be fruit. (A good source of potassium, but limit yourself to one per day.) If you eat tinned fruits – get the ones packed in natural, unsweetened juice instead of syrup. Empty several tins into Tupperware containers, and keep them in the fridge. Much more exciting as a quick snack than boring old carrot sticks.

Although fruit is a dieter's delight, it is certainly not calorie-free. As with everything else, eat only when you are genuinely hungry. Furthermore, remember that sweet fruits taste that way because they contain a certain amount of natural sugar. So do fruit *juices* . . . even when the label reads, 'no sugar added'. The point is that calories hang out in everything except glasses of water, and the little squirts add up.

7. NEVER APPLY HEAT TO FOOD FROM THE BOTTOM

Do not fry. Nothing in this world *needs* to be fried in fat. If the recipe says, 'brown the meat before you add liquid' – don't. You won't taste the difference, and you'll save hundreds of calories. Boil or poach the occasional egg – or, if you must fry, cook omelettes in non-stick pans, and don't add butter. As a general rule, apply heat from above (grilling) or all around (roasting, boiling, steaming).

Wok Right in?

Many nutritionists and diet experts sing the praises of *stir-frying* as a method of low-fat cooking. I remain sceptical on two counts. First, I mistrust any form of food preparation which contains the word 'fry'. Diet friendly? Some hope! (Pigs might fry.) Second, stir-fried foods have the wrong 'aura'. They come on like fattening stuff, because they look tempting and taste too good. All that soy sauce, those crisp little water chestnuts, glazed bean sprouts and baby corn-cobs. Too exciting to encourage maximum weight loss. Very more-ish, and likely to stimulate appetite. Serious dieters, I believe, should steer clear. 'Just say no', and wok away.

8. MILK OF KINDNESS

Skimmed milk is *vital* to a successful diet; move heaven and earth to get it. You soon get used to the taste, and prefer it to the cloying, creamier stuff. Don't claim that you don't *drink* milk or only use it in coffee. Everyone takes a swig after a bar of chocolate, uses it in cooking, puts it on breakfast cereal. And, when you open a new pint, do you really pour away that fat-intensive, calorie-laden top? Of course not. Who are you kidding? Serious dieters switch to skimmed.

Semi-Skimmed is for Wimps

No cheating, either, with 'semi-skimmed' – which is for wimps only, and nearly as bad as full cream milk. Remember that successful weight loss requires a very restricted calorie intake, and the difference between skimmed and semi-skimmed on your cornflakes and in coffee may be worth 150 calories a day. Anyway, heaven does not reward dieters unwilling to forgo this modicum of pleasure in the interests of a leaner, trimmer figure.

17
CLOTHING AND FAT
Fear and Self-Loathing in Department Stores

There is nothing more depressing than *shopping* when you feel *fat*. You search for clothes which make you feel better, but your state of mind gets progressively worse. No creature in the world seems as hateful as the one you see in the three-way mirror. You mistake yourself for Jebba the Hut. Morale at low ebb, you toss offending garments at the fitting-room wall, and go home – pausing only to devour a Danish at the in-store coffee shop. (Your punishment for being ugly is to make yourself *uglier*.)

People who carry too much weight (even, by their own standards, a *bit* too much) soon lose interest in fashion. They are not *comfortable* in clothes. Size, fit and style present problems for them. New clothes do not enhance appearance or bring happiness ... but serve only to remind them of how much they've expanded since the last time they shopped.

The whole process is torment for fatties. Garments frustrate and rebuke them. High fashion – unforgiving and unflattering to all but perfect figures – infuriates them. Clothing pulls under bulky arms, and binds at waistlines. It forms ridges where it spans broad backs or bottoms. It refuses to 'hang' well (or at all!) and seems designed to emphasize every flaw. Fatties fall back on loose, dark or boring garments, hoping to hide surplus weight. They use clothing as *camouflage*. This is 'negative dressing', and does not work. It is like trying to conceal the British Museum with a tarpaulin.

The hard fact is that *diet* is the only solution. No piece of apparel yet created by the fashion industry effectively disguises spare pounds. Kaftan or 'tent' shapes hang *out* instead of straight down, while tight things look set to burst like sausage skins. Girdles and corsets do not make fat women look slim – just constricted – and eye-catching patterns fail to draw attention away from flab. Too often, overweight people look not so much dressed as *upholstered*. All clothes become disappointing . . . an un-happy compromise instead of a pleasant boost to morale.

This is not to imply that only slim people should bother to get dressed in the morning. It's just that it's hard to look your best while trying to keep your body under wraps. People of most shapes can look perfectly *presentable*. They can be neat, tidy and well-groomed. They cannot, on the other hand, look great in clothes. 'Great in clothes' is reserved for *thin* people.

In fact, the first sign that your diet is working – that you are starting to achieve your 'target' weight – is when interest in shopping reawakens. The prospect of revealing your shape is no longer painful, and may even be a matter of pride. (Finances permitting, progress should be rewarded. Feel free, at this point, to buy something to boost your ego . . . since the best incentive to looking *better* is looking *good*.)

WHOSE FAULT IS IT, ANYWAY?

As ever, there's a school of thought which claims that the media are to blame. Magazines, it's said, should display clothes on models – both male and female – who are built less like stick insects, and more like 'average' consumers. Chances are that *this will never happen*. Editors are canny enough to reflect average *aspirations* rather than average *shapes*. Most of us aspire to be slim, young and beautiful . . . and few of us wish to see

Armani's latest collection on a bevy of prolapsed 'wrinklies' with protruding tums.

To appear to best advantage – either in the pages of a magazine or in real life – clothing must 'fall' properly. The less of *you* there is to get in the way, the better *it* hangs. Lycra, of course, needs a bit of you to cling to . . . but only a bit. The key to wearing 'stretch' fabrics is that they need to be S-T-R-E-T-C-H-E-D . . . not D-I-S-T-O-R-T-E-D.

Manufacturers, too, seem reluctant to accommodate the full range of human shapes. This is clear from the narrow selection of sizes they produce. If you're female, and smaller than a size 8 – forget it. Bigger than a 14? Get lost. And, when it comes to the tiny, 'second skin' lycra garments we all adore, there's an even more *limited* choice.

LYCRA GARMENTS
(Range of standard sizes)

LARGE   (thin)
MEDIUM (skinny)
SMALL   (anorexic)

For men, the situation is similar. *Big* men (say, the size of the average Texan) are, in retailing terms, *outré* . . . freaks of nature, consigned to specialist 'outsize' shops. Department stores carry a good selection of shirts for fellows who can wear size 14 collars. They've got suits and trousers aplenty to fit male models, hairdressers and airline cabin staff. But there's little for the 'beefier' customer. It's hard to miss the main marketing message:

that it's the consumer's job to tailor his body to fit available sizes . . . not the other way around.

You can be forgiven for concluding that all this is a marketing, manufacturing and retailing *conspiracy*: cynical, and cost effective. It's an accepted fact that *half* the females in the country wear a size 16 – or over. But, they are systematically ignored. Manufacturers know that they are dissatisfied with their bodies . . . and therefore spend little on clothing. They shop seldom, and dress economically – in the interests of decency, not fashion or style. Producers who wish to increase sales and profit prefer to target that narrow band of skinnies who 'look great in clothes', and spend, spend, spend accordingly.

It's hardly surprising that some heavyweights kick against the traces. '*Big*' they venture, '*is beautiful.*' Sick of altering seams and hems, they go to work instead on public perceptions. '*If you've got it,*' insist fatties, '*flaunt it!*' The theory is that *more than one* standard of beauty is acceptable. To count as 'attractive', you needn't conform to norms set in the pages of *Vogue* or *Elle*. Weigh 14 stone? OK – so you'll never be a pixie. Forget formfitting fabrics. Instead, opt for a generous kaftan in bright, primary colours. All eyes will be upon you . . . which is, after all, the objective. Right?

Depends on whether you want to look your best . . . or merely stop traffic. Grand gestures do certainly draw attention. But, for most people – Sandra Bernhard and Dame Edna apart – flamboyance is not enough. In most cases, it is a poor substitute for the rewards of genuine slimness.

DRESSING ON A DIET

While dieting – and on the way to your target weight – it is important to provide yourself with encouragement. You need sartorial *incentives*. The phrase 'feeling good about yourself' is much overworked ... but, as part of your weight-reduction plan, it is essential. Look and dress like a slob-ette, and the temptation to eat like one is overwhelming. So: *prepare to spend money*. Not lots, but some. Consider what you've saved by not purchasing 'formula' diets or plastic food. Invest it *now*.

THE 'NOW' RULES

RULE ONE

Do not wait until you've 'lost all the weight' to buy new clothing. Purchase some pieces NOW. Alter other garments to fit NOW... Even if you have to fix them again later.

RULE TWO

NEVER *buy clothes several sizes too small as an 'incentive' to lose more weight. Small clothes are merely depressing. Chances are that you'll never wear them.*

Live for the present. Look good NOW. Boost morale NOW.

Having starved assiduously, permit yourself to enjoy the pay-off. The better you look – the more pride you have in your appearance – the more 'staying power' you'll have for your diet.

Anyway, until the day when you emerge sylph-like – with curves made to be seen in designer jeans or Madonna's corselettes – consider yourself work-in-progress. Here are a few handy hints:

HOW TO SHOP 'THIN'

1. SLACK JACKET

A well-cut jacket is a great investment. For men and women, it can cover a multitude of sins. Make sure it's loose enough so that it just 'skims the body'. You should be able to raise your elbows to shoulder level, and pull both arms forward without feeling too constricted. A jacket, shirt or top is too small for you if it 'binds' under the arms, or forms ridges (or bulges) across your back when both arms are down at your sides. Before buying, always check the rear view in a three-way mirror. (This is good shopping practice whether you are thin or fat.) If the jacket is shaped, make sure that the waist hits at *your* waist, or immediately below. Short-waisted garments are uncomfortable, look outgrown, and make you feel fat.

2. WAIST OF EFFORT

Waistbands are the most reliable indicators of weight loss or gain. They are even more accurate than the bathroom scale! If last season's skirts or trousers feel snug around the middle, it's a fair bet that:

    a. they did not shrink in dry cleaning

    b. it's not because you're due for a period.

Chances are that *You're fatter*. Especially if straight skirts or classic slim-cut trousers are also tight at the hips.

Where possible, always choose skirts and trousers with *no waistbands*. Much women's apparel is now constructed in this way. It is more comfortable, and – unless you're Scarlett O'Hara with an 18 inch waist – more flattering. Specially to be avoided are wide, high waistbands. They may be OK while you're standing up – but, sink into a chair, and they displace spare cellulite, forcing it into unsightly bulges above and below.

Finally, there's something *psychological* about tight waistbands. By constricting your tum, they make you feel fat. You hate yourself, and perversely eat more. Subconsciously, you want to defeat and punish the straining fabric by bursting it . . . and liberating your tum.

3. TRY ON LOTS OF CLOTHES – WHETHER OR NOT YOU INTEND TO PURCHASE

This is particularly easy in large department stores, where sales staff are busy, and more than happy to ignore you. By freely trying and experimenting with different styles, you'll soon develop an idea of what best suits you at this 'transitional' stage. No need to worry about price, since you're not buying . . . you're *shopping*. There's a difference.

Before making any purchase, stop to look in a three-way mirror. If the store doesn't have one, ask for a large-ish hand mirror, and check out all angles. Buying clothes without a rear-view mirror is as foolhardy as *driving* without one. It can cause serious accidents.

A softly gathered skirt may appear to disguise a large tum when viewed from the *front* – but call to mind an elephant in a tutu when seen in *profile*. Pay special attention to the rear view of *trousers*, always a problem area. Does fabric cup, pull or, alternatively, droop under your bottom? Does it 'cut' in the crotch, especially when you sit down? (Try it!) Does your posterior resemble an inverted pair of McDonald's golden arches? If so – shop further.

4. BEWARE OF CLINGY FABRICS

They may adhere beautifully to Cindy Crawford (so, by all accounts, does Richard Gere) – but she is 6 feet tall, and bulge-free. Ordinary mortals have bra-lines, panty-lines, tummies, midriffs, bottoms, thighs . . . and even nipples. All these features are revealed by clingy clothes. Fortunate Cindy has no such body parts. Or, at least, not so's you'd notice in *Vogue* spreads. Richard does not seem to mind.

When dieters dress – weight and texture of fabric are

important. If fatties avoid garments which fit like cling-film, they should also reject the 'heavy stuff' which is not so much sewn as *engineered*. No point in adding bulk with industrial strength clothing, nubbly or hairy fabrics. (Deep-pile mohair sweaters, for example, are seldom a good choice.) Instead, choose something lightweight . . . but not too revealing. If a skirt or dress flows and moves nicely, it's the best camouflage for figure faults.

5. TENT-SHAPED GARMENTS DO NOT DISGUISE FAT

Overweight people often dress in large, enveloping shapes, hoping to conceal the size of the problem. They rely heavily upon the oversized shirt, sweater – or even coat. The difficulty is that yards of spare fabric tends to disguise *shape* . . . but emphasize *girth*. It's a poor trade-off. Remember Mama Cass in a kaftan? Unless you are virtually 'off the map' in terms of available sizes, it is probably a bad idea to cloak yourself in something resembling a pup tent with armholes.

To prove a point: consider the Arab ladies often seen swathed head to toe in dark fabric, leaving just a tiny slit for their eyes. Can you tell what they look like? No. Can you tell the *thin* ones from the *fat* ones? No problem!

While we're on this point, when shopping also remember not to be taken in by the *greatest lie in retailing*:

ONE SIZE FITS ALL

It doesn't. It is an unflattering compromise for everyone.

This idea belongs in the same category with the *shoe department's* favourite lie:

THEY'LL STRETCH WHEN YOU WEAR THEM

6. BLACK IS BEAUTIFUL

Black is a female fatty's best friend. It *does* make you look thinner . . . thinner, at any rate, than most colours. You will probably feel happiest in it while dieting – so feel free to wear it a lot. If you think it looks 'dead', try setting it off with gold jewellery, or strong accent colours.

To create the illusion of extra height or slenderness, keep tights, boots or shoes dark as well. When you mix black and coloured clothing, use black on your heaviest part (cover hips, for example, with a black skirt) and reserve accent colours (say, a bright shirt) for the (relatively) thin bits. If there are *no* relatively thin bits, wear only black, and paint your fingernails red.

7. LEGGING IT

Leggings. Fashion's new 'staple' – the most basic, revolutionary and successful garment to come off designer drawing-boards for years. As popular as the ubiquitous T-shirt. More comfortable than jeans – and more adaptable. Dress-them-up-or-down. Flattering to all shapes. Something for everyone.

Sold? I'm not. How can the most revealing piece of ready-to-wear ever created flatter 'all' figures? Frankly, it doesn't. Even when paired with long, generous jackets or voluminous tops, leggings can make fat calves look fatter, and emphasize well-rounded bottoms. They should be worn with care. Especially if they're brightly-patterned (Pucci or animal) prints, or light in colour (this includes grey). OAPs should probably forget leggings, whether their legs are thin or fat.

Dieters should take careful – and objective – note of figure flaws before making a legging decision. Once again, use that three-way mirror. If your legs are slim-ish from mid-thigh down, then fine. If not – or if your bottom and tum, protruding in opposite directions, are likely to be emphasized by the close attentions of stretch fabric – think again. A well-cut jacket or top may solve the problem. If not, confine legging-wearing to private moments at home ... at least until you've shed a few pounds. We've all winced at the sight of leopard-print leggings with spots distorted by the demands of hefty hips and thighs. Cruelty to animals.

8. WHEN STARVING GETS TOUGH – THINK SHOPPING

Will-power weakening? Gotta have that devil's food cake or banana nut muffin? Hold everything. Make yourself a promise ... and *keep* it! Practise THIN-THINK, which goes something like this:

THIN-THINK

Get stuffed, muffin. I can handle this. Just a few more hours, and then it's *tomorrow*. Tomorrow, the moment of temptation will be past. Tomorrow, I'll *shop*! The muffin will be history . . . and I'll feel *thin* in my clothes. My *new* clothes, which will look terrific, because I didn't eat the muffin. Shopping will be a pleasure. (I may look for leggings . . .)

REMEMBER:

Shopping (and trying on clothes) is not only an important incentive, and good dieters' therapy . . . but – best of all – *it consumes more calories*! *Shopping* (thank you, God) is *exercise*!

Just one word of warning: fatties of both sexes will do well to receive with scepticism the advice and/or praise of sales assistants. While dieting, shop to your heart's content . . . but 'let the (fat) buyer beware.'

Lies Which Sales Assistants Tell to Female Fatties:

a. One size fits all.

b. The shoes will stretch when you wear them.

c. You're thin enough already!

d. Don't worry. It's just that continental styles run small.

e. You're not a *true* size 16.

f. There's *plenty* of room across the hips.

g. It's supposed to look snug.

h. We're out of black. But the red looks lovely with your hair.

i. Another lady bought one this morning. She was *much* larger than you, and she looked *lovely*, didn't she, Tracy?

j. Another lady bought one this morning. She was really thin, and she looked *dreadful*, didn't she, Tracy?

Lies Which Sales Assistants Tell to Male Fatties:

a. You're not a *true* size 46. The jackets run small.

b. They make them in Italy, sir. They're cut for Italian men.

c. You won't want to do up the top button anyway, will you, sir?

d. The pleats in the trousers hang very well. Perfectly relaxed.

e. *Everyone* can wear jeans.

f. Take the 'extra large'. Only because sweaters should look big and roomy.

g. We consider a size 17½ collar *average*.

h. It's the fashion, sir. This season's neckties are cut short.

i. The shoes will stretch when you wear them.

j. The socks will stretch when you wear them.

k. I didn't hear the sound of ripping. (Did *you* hear the sound of ripping, Gary?)

18
THIN-THINK
A New Mind-Set for Would-Be Skinnies

If you've been on a diet for more than six hours, you'll know that doctors and other 'professionals' in this area are of limited help. The problem is that they tell fatties only *half* the real story. They are, of course, quick to point out what to eat and (longer list) what to *reject*. But they rarely touch upon (and, indeed, seem unaware of!) the *key* to successful weight loss: the *mystery 'X' factor*. This has more to do with *attitude* than with food.

Veteran slimmers know well that much of dieting is 'in the mind' . . . that it is just as important to learn to *think thin* as to change eating habits. It is, in fact, the successful co-ordination of mind and body which wins the day, and finally transforms a former fatty into a life-long skinny.

Whatever doc may say – DIETING IS NOT AN EXACT SCIENCE. Calorie-counts make weight loss sound simple: just follow the numbers, connect the dots, and you're sure to emerge sylph-like in the end. The truth is that the bodies – and minds – of fatties behave in a more random fashion. Every dieter is familiar with the ways in which his or her system seems to defy accepted 'norms': the glitches, the metabolic idiosyncrasies, the *psychological barriers.* No medical book acknowledges them. Few doctors address them. But every fatty is acutely aware of them. No diet can succeed without taking them into account, and suggesting 'coping strategies'. So, here is:

THIN-THINK:

(Twenty-one Essential Rules for Dieters)

---

1. MAKE SURE YOU'RE HUNGRY

Before you eat a morsel – stop. Think. Feel. *Make sure you're hungry!* If not, delay eating (even carrot sticks) until you are. Resolve that, from now on, food intake must *always* be associated with *hunger*. Just bored? Read a book. Depressed? Go shopping.

Furthermore, try not to 'eat to schedule'. It may well be lunchtime, but – unless you are hungry – there is no compelling reason to eat. For all of us – and fatties in particular – food is part of the rhythm of our lives. It punctuates the day, and moves it forward. In the minds of fatties, therefore, it becomes easily separated from its main function. Neo-skinnies must break the habit of eating out of a sense of momentum, habit or routine. It's vital to re-establish the direct link between food and hunger . . . and the first step is to make sure you're in touch with your tummy's real needs.

2. DON'T MISTAKE 'HUNGRY' FOR 'THIRSTY'

Nutritionists claim that many dieters register 'hunger' when they are, in fact *thirsty*. So, when you feel the urge to eat, take a moment to reflect. Would a drink do? If in doubt, start with a glass of water. It can't hurt – and may do the trick.

Most sensible diets recommend at least six large glasses of water per day. Fluids are, of course, essential to health, and water is diet-friendly in many ways. In combination with food, it creates a 'full' feeling without adding calories, and helps to 'flush' the system and keep you regular. Do not fear that drinking lots of water will cause you to look or feel 'bloated'. The reverse is generally true. But – in the interests of health *and* to prevent water retention – cut down on salt.

Eau Great

Feel free to drink Perrier or Evian (or similar) with everything. It looks sophisticated. It's calorie-free. No one can tell there's no vodka in it. And all those little bubbles are so filling!

Bed or Breakfast?

While we're at it – don't mistake *tired* for *hungry*. The impulses to eat, drink and sleep seem surprisingly easy to confuse. When tired (4 p.m. 'droop') and in need of a lift, fatties reach automatically for a snack when a few minutes of shut-eye would do. True, it's not always possible to grab forty winks. But, do learn to identify the *difference* . . . and, when the opportunity arises – catnap. It does more for your figure than a Kit Kat any day.

FAT-THINK   THIN-THINK

3. EAT YOUR LAST FULL MEAL SIX HOURS BEFORE BEDTIME

Obviously, this allows adequate time to digest and burn what you've eaten. Fattening late snacks or rich, milky drinks are the world's best way to hoard calories. While dieting, try to go to bed each night feeling *slightly* hungry; you'll find that minor pangs soon subside when you've hit the hay. A bit of emptiness is, after all, a positive sign that your diet is working. If you just can't sleep, then you're *too* hungry . . . so, drink your skimmed milk or eat a piece of fruit, and try again.

Tip:

A good trick for creating that 'satisfied' feeling just before bed: try approximately two tablespoons of Quaker Puffed Wheat or Puffed Rice (two of the lowest-calorie cereals on the market) in one cup of skimmed milk. This small amount provides approximately 80 calories ... just enough to make you *temporarily* comfortable. Now, here's the real trick: *Go right to sleep while the feeling lasts.* Do not stop to read, or your tummy will start to rumble, and you'll need to eat again. With any luck, you'll be unconscious before you know you're miserable.

Another temporary appetite-killer: a hot bath before bedtime. All that blood rushing away from your tummy to the surface of your skin will alleviate hunger, and produce a pleasant sedative effect. If *that* doesn't work, try reading a collection of selected speeches by John Major.

4. SLOBS RULE, OK

Hungry like the wolf? Then, eat your diet snack straight out of containers in the fridge. Tear at it, get your face in it, let it trickle down your arm if you like. Who's looking? When ravenous, don't stop to transfer food to *dishes*. You won't be able to cope with the time-lag. Anyway, bad enough you have to diet ... who wants to wash up?

5. DO TAKE VITAMINS

They may be good for you. (No one knows for sure.) At any rate, they're something else to *eat*. Take large ones, with plenty of water at bedtime.

6. ALWAYS CARRY OLD FOOD

Never be caught short. When dieting successfully, one thing is certain: you're going to be *hungry* a lot. Sometimes suddenly, urgently and hysterically. If you're unprepared (inadequately supplied with diet snacks) you'll succumb to the nearest Custard Cream. Any Hostess Twinky will regard you as a pushover.

So don't forget to slip a slice or two of this morning's wholemeal bread or toast (unbuttered, of course) in a self-sealing bag, and pop it into your briefcase or handbag. You can also choose a 'dry' fat-free bagel, some melba toast, an apple or similar. Remember: nothing *too* attractive or enticing – and, preferably, something you don't much care for. That way, you won't be tempted to take it out and eat it unless you're *desperate* . . . in which case, it'll come in handy.

Feel free to abandon your old toast after four or five days, when it it has definitely lost its charm. You know it's past its best when it begins to taste like the inside of your handbag.

7. JUST SAY 'NO'

Nancy Reagan understood this one. It is possible to form the *habit* of refusal. 'No' gets easier with practice, and – you'll find – only hurts for a moment. Say you're dining with friends at a restaurant. Everyone orders dessert. 'No, thanks,' you say firmly, looking past the sweet trolley and straight into the waiter's eye. 'Just a cappuccino for me.' 'Oh, c'mon!' they all cry. 'It's a special occasion!' 'No, I'm fine,' you insist. 'Maybe I'll have some of *yours*.' This usually keeps everyone quiet.

Say whatever you like. If you're confident, you'll prevail. If resolve starts to slip – or you make accidental eye-contact with the *crème brûlée*, simply *look around*. Notice the people who *are* 'tucking in'. Chances are that you don't wish to look like them. Then; *think ahead*. Once this difficult moment is past, there's all of *tomorrow*. Tomorrow, you'll be glad you said 'no'. Tomorrow, you'll feel so much better getting dressed, so much better in your clothes, so much better about yourself if you've forgone the (fleeting) pleasure of the sweet trolley. If, on the other hand, you weaken, tomorrow morning will look gloomy. Dessert will be history, but its legacy will linger on.

8. 'BITE IS RIGHT': (THE ART OF 'DAMAGE LIMITATION')

One of the worst features of dieting is that it is socially isolating. Food is, in California-speak, a 'sharing' experience, and makes you feel 'part of the gang'. When everyone else eats, and you abstain ... you feel you're missing something, even if (and, take careful note of your own feelings) you're not *really hungry*. Habitual dieters feel sorry for themselves – and chronically *deprived*.

The best way to cope with this over the long haul is to take *bites* of the things you adore. This requires willpower, but beats total abstinence any day. Is the family sharing a meltingly wonderful birthday cake? No need to feel left out. Cut yourself a *small* slice (more like a 'sliver') – take two bites – and then *stop*. Yes, you *can*! Forbidden foods do little damage when eaten in minute quantities. A bite or two of something irresistible is relatively harmless ... and may ease you past a difficult moment.

True, one luxurious bite-sized chocolate champagne truffle can be worth 100 concentrated calories – so, if you must taste it, take a *small* bite, and (here's the hard part) *abandon* the rest. Give it to a skinny friend. Feed it to an obliging Airdale. Throw it away . . . or – better still – leave it in the fridge, wrapped in cling film, awaiting your next sugar crisis. With any luck, you can spin out one truffle for at least six months. (This confuses fat cells, which are unable to handle so irregular an intake. They become bewildered, and wander off.)

Once you've had a bite or two, you have enjoyed the pleasure of eating, and made yourself part of the shared experience. Your next job is to *pretend* that you've eaten larger amounts. Remember the fundamental truth about eating: *once it's over, it's over.* It matters little whether you've had two bites or twenty . . . the food is gone. At this stage, if you'd eaten the whole serving, you'd probably *still* want more. Seconds, perhaps. Conclusion: you gain nothing from a larger portion except weight. So, *taste* it – stop early – then imagine you've eaten it all. It's not *quantity* which produces satisfaction; it's *participation*.

FAT-THINK

It's no use.

Once I start, I can't stop . . .

Gotta *finish* that slice of fudge cake.

Any spare whipped cream?

THIN-THINK

Profiteroles . . . my fave!

Be still, my beating heart.

OK . . . pass me *one*.

Anyone want half??

9. SOMEONE ELSE'S CALORIES

Few doctors know this, but it is a scientific fact: SOMEONE ELSE'S CALORIES ARE LESS FATTENING THAN YOUR OWN. When in restaurants, you should wait until *others* order dessert – or the marvellous fettucini in cream sauce which you secretly crave. When the time seems right, ask nonchalantly for a bite. (Friends and lovers will normally pass you a big one, which you can make into two.) This is even better than ordering the dish yourself. You know what it tastes like. You experience eating it – but remain virtuous.

Best of all, you have once again out-manoeuvred and foiled the plans of malevolent little calories. They are under the clear impression that they've been served to *someone else*. Primed to target another metabolism and bond with a different set of fat cells, they harmlessly bypass *yours*. (Effectively, you are 'laundering' calories.)

Made for Sharing

Whether at home or out, seize every opportunity to share *portions*. (Do not confine sharing to Quality Street or desserts.) No harm in dividing a heaped plate of pasta, or a large salad. Sharing is part of the art of damage limitation. It insures that no one can eat too much. Frankly, most people are served (and eat) portions twice as big as they really need. It's often practical to cut them in half. When the meal is over, and food has 'registered', you'll usually find that you've had enough. If not – you can always eat *more*. (Once you've over-eaten, you can't take it back.)

These days, people are glad enough to share. First, everyone's weight-watching. In restaurants, sharing provides a chance to 'sample' foods without making a nutritional commitment. It's economical. Best of all, it's *politically correct*. There's a very New Age feeling to making do with a single order of goat cheese on radic-chio. It is environmentally sound. You are not only dieting, but saving the planet.

Notes on sharing:

NOTE ONE:

> *Women* happily share food with other women.
>
> *Men* share food with women (if forced).
>
> *Both* are prepared to share food with children.
>
> *Real men* do not share food with other *men*.
> To do so invites suspicion.
> (Real men don't share quiche.)

NOTE TWO:

Dieting women should *always* endeavour to share portions with *men*. This helps to keep your weight down, because men *cheat*. They eat faster than you, and take bigger bites. They consume far more than their fair share, then pretend that it was accidental, and they didn't notice.

10. DELIBERATELY KILL YOUR OWN APPETITE

Serious dieters should never confront a meal on an empty stomach. Why invite temptation? It goes without saying that *hungry people eat more*. (It's equally foolhardy to visit the supermarket when ravenous.)

The trick here is to set aside the admonitions of generations of parents: 'If you eat that apple before dinner, Norman, you'll ruin your appetite!' Your job is to *deliberately* spoil your own appetite before Force 9 starvation sets in. An apple or a piece of (unbuttered) wholemeal toast at noon takes 'the edge' off lunch at 1 p.m. A very low fat plain yogurt laced with a few drops of coffee essence does the same trick at 5 p.m., in time for dinner.

This is part of your *grazing* pattern, and is simply a means of spreading a restricted calorie intake more evenly through the day. Glasses of mineral water before meals are also useful as 'spoilers'.

Spoiling the Fun

Blunting your own appetite makes it easier to limit intake when you finally sit down to a meal. But, when 'spoiling', do not expect to *enjoy* yourself. The best spoilers are filling – but deeply uninteresting. When you've worked up a good, healthy appetite, they are profoundly disappointing. This is as it should be. So, it's pointless to complain, 'I'm not hungry for an apple!' Of course you're not! But, food *preference* – when you're dieting – has nothing to do with it. It's a luxury you can't afford. (Show me the person who genuinely prefers a raw apple to a toasted cheese sandwich and I'll show you some kind of a dork.) It goes without saying that wannabe skinnies must keep an eye on the long-term objective.

A FINAL NOTE:
If you're really hungry, you'll *want* the apple. You may even enjoy it. *If not* – and you're serious about dieting – eat it anyway.

Remember that, with luck, life's *ordinary events* may intervene, and help you to 'apply the brakes' to your appetite:

11. DON'T MISTAKE 'EAT' FOR 'NEAT'

Some people eat out of a sense of tidiness. They take a container of ice cream, and try to make the top smooth. They polish off the leftovers on their children's plates. By eating, they impose a sense of order and symmetry on life. This is a shortcut to disaster.

Furthermore, if you're planning to go out, resist advice to 'eat so you won't be hungry'. Take a snack with you if necessary, but eat only when you *are* hungry . . . and never use food as a form of prevention.

12. THE POWER OF LATERAL THINKING

When dieting, rule *nothing* out. If it's effective motivation –and harmless to health – *go for it*. For example:

> **Roseanne Barr on 'diets':**
>   'My husband and I are on a drastic diet.
>   You have to eat every meal *naked*, in front of a mirror.
>   Some restaurants have a problem with that.'

13. WELCOME BOREDOM

Do not try too hard to fight nutritional boredom while losing weight by 'varying' menus to inject 'excitement' into your diet. If experts were honest, they'd tell you that variety, excitement – and, for that matter, *enjoyment* – are more or less inconsistent with successful weight loss. You must, of course, achieve a basic nutritional balance in what you eat. Essential vitamins and minerals can be found in a wide variety of foods – but fatties should choose only the ones which are 'diet friendly'. This strictly limits the possibilities. Iron, for example, is present in a range of foods which include vegetables and calves' liver. Since the liver is high in cholesterol and will (if eaten regularly) definitely s-t-r-e-t-c-h your Lycra, the choice is clear.

Once you've devised a formula 'eating plan' which delivers the minimum daily adult requirement on 1,000 to 1,500 calories a day – *stick with it*! It's like mastering a Rubik's Cube. You may never be able to repeat the trick.

Sure, you can play around at the edges. Tinker with your menu, and amuse yourself by making small adjustments. There's the pulsating excitement, for instance, of occasionally swapping unbuttered courgettes for unbuttered sprouts. But, that's not the point. Serious dieters should not *fight* boredom . . . but *welcome* it.

Here's why:

As it is, fatties spend too much time thinking about food. The beauty of a simple, limited (but tolerable) daily eating plan – with perhaps three basic menus each for lunch and dinner – is that it allows you to *forget* about food. No need to *think* about what you're going to eat . . . you *know*! No need to count calories . . . you've *done* that! At last, you can relax. As you rule out variety, you also eliminate uncertainty. Just stick to your trusty nutritional blueprint for X number of weeks, exercise as directed – and weight loss is assured. (Fatties want guarantees.)

This accounts for the popularity of 'meal replacement' diets. Dieters like them because such 'formulas' demand few choices (you get the nauseating 'chocolate' shake unless you prefer the revolting 'cherry') and seem to promise results. But, why fill your body with chemicals, when you can create the same *reassuring sense of monotony* with *real food*? Having devised your daily diet, you're safe. Bored, but safe. For fatties, boredom is liberating.

14. DESIGN YOUR PERSONAL DIET PLAN
(*Keep It Simple*)

To maintain my weight, I eat (more or less) the same thing every day. At 5′4″ in height, it keeps me at a nice, even 8 stone. Many will no doubt consider my diet stupifyingly dull, but, when I'm hungry enough (which is always) I actually enjoy it. Best of all – as long as I stick to the plan, I can be reasonably sure that I'm safe. My body won't spring any nasty surprises on me (like a 6 pound overnight weight gain).

JANE'S MAINTENANCE DIET

Breakfast

A cup of bran flakes in two cups of skimmed milk. No sugar.

Mid-Morning

One slice of unbuttered wholemeal bread. (This can be toasted, if preferred.) One cup of coffee with skimmed milk. No sugar.

Lunch

Small plate (approximately one and a half cups) mixed raw vegetable salad. (No dressing.) Variations may include:

    a. cucumber, sweetcorn, broccoli, and a few lima
       or kidney beans

    b. tomato, fresh sliced mushroom, mange-tout and
       bean sprouts.

plus:

One serving of mixed fruit salad (say, apple,
orange, melon, pineapple – and a strawberry or
grape or two).

plus:

One slice of unbuttered wholemeal bread or toast,
or a hot brown roll without butter.

plus:

At least one large glass of water. Coffee or tea
(with skimmed milk) if desired.

Mid-Afternoon

One medium-sized banana.

or:

A plain, very low fat yogurt;
or another slice of unbuttered wholemeal bread or
toast.

plus:

a medium-sized glass of tomato juice;
or a fresh orange;
and a cup of tea (skimmed milk, no sugar);
and a glass or two of mineral water.

Dinner

A glass of tomato or fresh orange juice;
or slice of melon or half grapefruit (no sugar);

or small mixed salad dressed with lemon juice or
balsamic vinegar;
or cup of clear or vegetable-based soup (no added
cream or grated cheese)

plus:

3–4 oz. grilled breast of chicken (remove skin);
or 3–4 oz. steamed, grilled or baked fish;
or (occasionally) 3–4 oz. lean beef (all visible fat
removed).

plus:

Generous portion of steamed (unbuttered)
vegetables;
or mixed salad (lightly dressed with balsamic
vinegar or lemon juice).

plus:

One half baked jacket potato (no butter);
or small portion of pasta with tomato sauce;
or small serving of steamed or boiled rice (white,
brown, or 'wild');
or white or brown bread (no butter).

plus:

Dessert of fresh fruit or fruit salad (no cream)
including one or two prunes;
coffee or tea with skimmed milk;
lots of mineral water.

Optional

Half glass of red or white wine with dinner.

Note:

As a variation, try an occasional 'main course
salad':

Slimmer's Salad Niçoise:
Lettuce, radicchio, tomato, cucumber, 2–3 oz. of (drained) tuna packed in water or brine, one or two hard-boiled egg whites (no yolks!). Sprinkle with capers, if liked . . . or a few plainly boiled pasta shapes.

Dress with a 'dash' of olive oil (no more than one tablespoon), and vinegar.

Slimmer's Pasta Salad:
Lettuce, tomato, cucumber, sliced raw mushrooms, raw broccoli, and any plain pasta shapes you like (*not* the varieties 'stuffed' with meat or cheese). Other raw vegetables – i.e. carrots, beans, celery or cauliflower – can also be added. Sprinkle with fresh tarragon. Toss in dressing as above.

Before Bed (*only if hungry*):

2 tablespoons Puffed Wheat or Puffed Rice cereal with a half cup of skimmed milk;
or small portion pineapple (fresh, or tinned in natural juice);
or small glass of fresh orange juice.

plus:
Final glass of mineral water.

if *not* hungry:
Final glass of mineral water.

You can go on like this for years and years. If you don't like the dishes suggested, you'll quickly find your own variations on the theme ... bearing in mind that you don't have much scope for excitement without adding calories.

It's pretty basic – but that's the whole idea. You need to devise a plan you can live with over the long haul. If your intention is to stay *permanently* slim, you can't do it with nutritional 'gimmicks' like 'meal replacements'. Since diets are forever, you've got to get to grips with *real food*.

Follow a plan similar to the one above, and you can confidently rule out any sharp fluctuations in weight.

15. SURVIVING A BLOW-OUT (*What if you break your diet?*)

Sooner or later, it happens to all slimmers ... particularly if you regard your 'diet' as a plan for life. You may be overwhelmed by temptation – or hunger. Sometimes you 'slip' because you feel rotten (emotionally or physically). Occasionally, events conspire against you (there you are in the Kalahari desert with only a packet of Maltesers between you and certain extinction). More often, you temporarily lose concentration – or incentive.

Limit Damage

If you can't resist breaking your diet, the first step in damage limitation is to avoid a full-scale blow-out. Make it your short-term goal to *cheat only a little*. Remind yourself that you'll suffer less remorse in the morning if you've kept the lid on, and resist indulging in an orgy of self-destruction.

Inadvertently eaten a *whole* French pastry without sharing? Tarte au shame! Chalk it up to experience, and *return to your diet eating-plan* for the rest of the day. Follow it as normal. Do *not*:

a. punish yourself, or try to 'compensate' by eating *no food* for the rest of the day

b. (worse still) throw caution to the winds, and binge.

Once you've crammed in a British Rail oversized chocolate chip cookie, or several servings of Wall's Viennetta (one slice is never enough) the tendency is to keep going. Carried away by remorse and self-loathing, you abandon all control, and do some industrial-strength eating.

In binge-mode, you consume – all at once – everything you've craved but denied yourself for weeks. You eat mayonnaise straight from the jar. You demolish a whole cheeseboard, pouring cream on the gorgonzola. You follow with a double banana split (six scoops), telling yourself that everyone is entitled to a cheese course *and* a sweet. At midnight, you find yourself melting marshmallows under the grill and spreading them on toast, so that you can cram all of your childhood favourites into one catastrophic day.

If this happens to you after a period of self-denial, write the day off – and *forgive yourself*. You're not alone. Who amongst us has not eyed a plain chocolate digestive biscuit, and posed The Fatty's Unanswerable Question:

WHY EAT ONE WHEN I COULD FINISH THE WHOLE PACKET?

Most important: return as quickly as possible to your 'normal' eating-plan. Do not – out of a sense of guilt or despair – extend the binge into Day Two. Remember that you've done no irreversible harm. You have not permanently 'ruined' anything. Your progress has suffered only a slight setback, which must be seen in context. After all, *diets are forever*. Winners – as has already been said – are those with staying-power.

On the Bright Side

Even blow-outs have a bright side. A certain amount of 'aversion therapy' is created during a binge, which is helpful in an extended diet. Fatties know that the attrac-

tion of 'forbidden' foods increases with time and separa-
tion, and preoccupies the mind: 'I'd kill for an egg and
bacon sarnie on fried bread!'

Eat three at once, and – with any luck – you'll feel
slightly nauseous. Better equipped to forgo them for
another long period. Positively *relieved* to return to fruit
salad. (OK, let's not get carried away.)

It is, however, far easier to diet again strenuously when
you've reminded yourself that all your old 'to die for'
favourites are good ... but not *that* good. Not as good,
for example, as slipping into a size 10 dress, and watching it fall comfortably. Not as good as catching the
admiring glances as you cavort in Lycra workout gear at
the local health club. Which brings us back to another
'coping' strategy:

16. REPOSITION YOUR PLEASURE

The pleasure derived from eating is – as we've noted –
short-lived. Food is only a pleasure for the brief time it
spends in your mouth. When it's anywhere else, it's a
real nuisance. On your plate, it's a decision, rebuke or
challenge. In your tummy, it's a regret. Food – to fatties
– is seldom a source of unfettered enjoyment.

Part of THIN-THINK, therefore, is learning to *reposition*
your pleasure. Instead of relying on food for your (fleeting) satisfaction, the idea is to think long-term. How
much more lasting will your pleasure be at seeing your
own slim shape reflected in a mirror – or in noting the
reactions of others? You will enjoy the satisfaction of
improved health and appearance, of classification as a

'slim' person, of feeling sexier and more confident. Best of all, you'll experience the pleasure of feeling 'in control' of your life.

Life in the Fat Lane

It is, quite simply, *better* to be slim than even a few pounds overweight. Better in ways you can't fully appreciate until it's happened to you. There's a clear sense of accomplishment and achievement. You've taken charge, and 'joined the club'. It may be anathema to many ... but thin people are insiders. In any competition, they have the inside track. By comparison, life in the fat lane runs a poor second.

No one claims that 'getting there' is a picnic. To become slim – and maintain your shape – you must *break* the automatic expectation of full enjoyment each time you sit down to eat. You are simply not going to enjoy your unsweetened oat bran or raw vegetable salad as much as saddle of lamb or boeuf Wellington and crème caramel. But, by golly, one of these days – long after the boeuf has faded from even Wellington's memory – you're going to enjoy the results!

17. DON'T USE FOOD TO PUNCTUATE THE DAY

One of the reasons food is so habit-forming is that we use it for far more than the simple satisfaction of appetite. It divides and *structures* our days. Meals and snacks are natural 'breaks' ... rewards for 'getting through' a number of hours. They mark progress, and time. Cutting them out (or making them shorter) is somehow disorient-ing and unsettling to fatties, who look around for an-other form of 'punctuation'. Some almost begin to wish that they smoked.

The best antidote is to *keep busy* – and think of other rewards. You can, of course, still rely on tea or coffee breaks, as long as you add only skimmed milk, and no sugar. But, consider this a golden opportunity to redis-cover life's *other* small pleasures:

FAT-THINK

a. What a workload!

b. If I get through to 4 o'clock, I'll reward myself with a jam tart and some cocoa.

THIN-THINK

If I get through to four o'clock, I'll stop for fifteen minutes, and:

a. re-read my love letters

b. try that new eye-shadow duo

c. listen to some Elton John/Rod Stewart/Phil Collins

d. watch a few minutes of tennis

e. walk down to the shops

f. henna my hair

g. flirt with someone down by the photocopier

h. make urgent, passionate love while I feel thin and *hungry*!

18. BREAK YOUR DIET REGULARLY

This may sound like perverse advice but, if you wish to become slim and stay that way, managed 'breaks' in a diet are essential. Remember that DIETS ARE FOR-

EVER; they don't 'end'. Total deprivation is therefore unrealistic ... whether you are trying to lose or maintain weight. Designing an eating-plan that is practical in the long term means including 'treats'. These should not be regarded as 'cheating' or 'set-backs'. They are simply a part of your overall diet strategy. Far better to 'regularize' such breaks than to succumb to random, uncontrollable binges.

If, for example, you adhere to a strict 1,200-calorie-a-day diet between Sunday and Friday, give yourself a break on Saturday. Choose your 'fave' food. Been longing for a spag bol, cod and chips, a pint of lager, half bottle of wine or a salami sandwich? Have it *now*. Eat *half* a portion if possible (see tips 8 and 9). Do *not* feel guilty. Three hundred to 500 spare calories on a Saturday will not 'undo' a week's good work. On the contrary: a treat may provide a 'boost', and make it possible for you to continue dieting. If fatties are prisoners of their own metabolic systems, this is 'time off' for good behaviour. In any case, learning to break a diet in a disciplined way (without gorging like a maniac) is good practice for the rest of life.

Once you've got the hang of it, you'll find that you're (relatively) happy with *small* portions of diet-busters. (Half a Toblerone tastes just as good as a whole one. And – since you're not going to be content with a whole one anyway – why eat more than half?) Sure, from time to time you'll long to roll in a fudge cake, or wade through a vat of double cream. You know the feeling. It is no longer enough to *eat* the food; you want to enjoy a *closer* physical relationship with it. Is it possible, you wonder, to have children with a cheesecake?

Remember, though, the bottom line. Experts calculate that *one pound* of body fat is worth 3,500 calories. This means that, for every pound you wish to lose, 3,500 calories must come out of the diet . . . not all at once, but over a period of time. Say that a woman of average build 'maintains' her weight on 2,000 calories a day (or 14,000 calories a week), but wishes to be slimmer. Her weight reduction diet will need to deliver 10,500 calories per week (or 1,500 a day) in order to produce a loss of one pound per week. That doesn't allow room for much cheating – or much cheese-cake – unless you're prepared to lose weight more slowly.

19. PROPER LIQUIDITY

Not a lot of people know this: there are one or two *unmistakable* signs that your diet is working, and you're losing weight. You can tell first thing in the morning – even *before* you step (gingerly) onto the bathroom scale. If waking up means an urgent dash to the loo, your body is working well to help you eliminate spare flab. The fewer calories you've consumed on the preceding day, the fuller your bladder is apt to be the following morning. Stuff yourself in the evening, and you're un-likely to experience the same 'dawn rush' of fluids. (Test it – and see if you agree.)

20. SEIZE EVERY OPPORTUNITY TO EAT ALONE

Let's face it: 'designer starvation' accommodates very little food per day. What's 1,000 calories? A plain skimmed milk yogurt, a few raw vegetables, a swig of orange juice and you're nearly there. One-third of your daily ration can slip down before you know it. Before you've even registered the fact that you're *eating*.

Fatties should not be embarrassed, therefore, to jealously guard precious eating-time. Give yourself a chance, each day, to *concentrate* on food. Otherwise, you'll feel doubly cheated. The point is that 'diet' food makes little or no impact in terms of enjoyment. Most of us can take or leave a carrot stick. (It hardly delivers the gastronomic 'kick' of pastrami on rye.) Above all, you need to pay close attention, or you'll miss it.

THEREFORE

DON'T feel compelled to make lively conversation while eating.

DON'T eat when you're rushed. Take time to taste and chew.

DON'T argue with the kids at mealtimes.

DON'T take phone calls. (Remove the phone from the hook.)

LOCK UP the cat.

FEEL PERFECTLY FREE, if necessary, to lock yourself in a bedroom with your bowl of bran flakes in order to protect eating-time.

OTHERWISE, by the time you've talked, gestured and swallowed, a large part of your daily nutritional allowance is gone . . . and you don't remember a thing.

21. LEARN TO THROW FOOD AWAY

This is a dieter's revenge – your only means of striking back at calories. So, be aggressive. Taken a bite of an illicit doughnut? Hurl the rest into the kitchen sink. Pulled a crisp from the packet? Dump what's left before you succumb. Wasteful, yes, but sinful, no.

Once, while dieting, I had a spiritual struggle with a blueberry muffin. I wanted it desperately, so I took a bite, and threw the rest into the waste bin. But, I couldn't stop thinking about it. Eventually, I stole back, and rescued the object of my desire. It was a low point. The muffin had cigarette ash on it. To my eternal shame, I ate it anyway.

My point is that diet, for many people, is a life-long battle of near-Olympian proportions; sometimes heroic, often not. Witness muffin. For that reason, there's some satisfaction to be found in taking physical *revenge* on food. Dumping a source of temptation into the nearest grubby receptacle shows it who's boss. (This is no more than it deserves for tormenting you, and making you fat.) Fatties have every right to pursue a ruthless vendetta against it. This is what is meant by FAT-WA.

19
FRIENDS AND FAT – 'DIET SABOTAGE'

Here is a valuable piece of advice for fatties:

DO NOT TELL FRIENDS YOU ARE DIETING ...
(*even if they are* also *dieting*).

True, such advice works against all received wisdom about the virtues of friendly support, dieters' 'self-help' groups ... and the psychological benefits of 'bonding'. But, the fact is that serious dieting is essentially a private matter – and your own concern. No matter how you dress it up, starving is a lonely activity. No one else can do it for you, or fully appreciate your discomfort. The supreme effort which finally shifts pounds and transforms your body must be yours alone. Rubbing up against other (fat) people does not really help much.

If you think about it, there's little to gain (and much to lose) by alerting others. You may feel tempted, of course, to solicit sympathy, endorsement or advice. But, remember that your diet is not 'public property'. It is a serious business – *your* business – and not a social event. You will have to decide, early on, which objective is more important: to be the centre of attention or to lose weight.

Three Reasons to Diet Discreetly

1. Your diet is *not* temporary. It is not going to be 'over' – though friends (if they're aware of it) will assume it is. What you are about to do is gradually – but permanently – change your lifestyle and habits. Those close to you, who've *shared* said habits, may have mixed feelings. They may lobby surprisingly hard for the return of 'the old you'. This is a pressure which will not help you, and which you needn't endure.

The changes you're about to make can be accomplished with subtlety and discretion. For example: you're going to use *real food*, and not plastic powders or 'meal replacements' (which are a dead giveaway). You're going to lead an active life, and exercise, and have fun, and buy clothes, and look great. No need to *announce* it . . . just get on with it. Unless tipped off, friends are unlikely to notice that you're 'dieting' until results begin to show.

2. Telling friends and relatives *invites interference* . . . and unwelcome comment. This can, at worst, sabotage and undermine your diet plans. At very least, it's bound to annoy you.

The very word 'diet' is provocative, and excites people. Many then feel entitled to: (a) thwart you or (b) patronize you. They may say: (a) 'But, you don't *need* to diet!' or (b) 'Thank goodness! You'll look so much better a few pounds thinner!' You will suspect the first group of hypocrisy. You will want to hit the second with a meat axe.

While dieting remain sceptical about the reactions of friends and family. Diets (yours) have a way of making others feel threatened and competitive. This is true whether they're thin or fat . . . because diets disrupt the 'status quo', and change the balance of power between people. You may suddenly emerge thinner and more attractive than friends. Your self-discipline and will-power may serve as an (unintended) rebuke to them. While professing support for your diet, some will behave badly. It's an observable fact that, when *you* starve, *others* get smaller.

3. There's an even more compelling reason for keeping your diet under wraps. Confide in friends, and they'll quickly spread the word to others. Soon, *everyone* knows. You're 'fair game' for snipers: a human target, a walking invitation. You've granted a *licence to interfere*:

    a. 'C'mon, Em . . . just one eensy "treat" won't hurt!'

    b. Sandra's slaved over her special Swiss roll, just for *you*.'

    c. 'Anyway, you've lost enough!'

OR,

    d. 'Drink up, Kev. Don't be a killjoy.'

    e. 'Can't say "no" to a free pint!'

    f. 'Still starving, mate? And all for the sake of Karen in Accounts.'

    g. 'Not *fat*! Isn't that right, everyone? He's not really *fat* . . .'

Worst of all, when you bring your diet to the attention of others, they feel fully entitled to pass comment on every mouthful:

'Salt's no good on a diet, Deb.'

'Look who's eating *bread*! I thought you were on a *diet*.'

'Slap wristies! Not another bite of that spaghetti!'

'Uh, uh! Too much sauce.'

'You're not snacking *again*, are you?'

OR, ALTERNATIVELY:

'Only veggie salad? Aren't you MEGA-hungry?'

Give friends an opening, and you risk losing the initiative. This is *your* diet. Do not allow it to be hijacked by others. For better or worse – make your own decisions.

Things to practise saying to friends:

'I'm the Greatest Living Authority on what I can – and can't – eat.'

'Thank you, Dr Scarsdale.'

'When *I've* decided I'm thin enough, you'll be the first to know.'

'Get lost.'

If dieting is a lonely activity, it must also be a *selfish* one. Make no apologies for putting your own needs first; and on no account allow others to undermine your efforts. *You* are Number One. Do not hesitate to bark at those who deserve it. If this leaves you – temporarily – with fewer friends than a Rottweiler, so be it. It's a small price to pay for looking great in Lycra.

Truth to tell, many former fatties need 'assertiveness' training. Typically, they have developed 'friendly', accommodating personalities to compensate for physical shortcomings. They have won friends by being easygoing . . . or downright compliant. But, successful dieting demands that they 'unlearn' old habits. As Bill Clinton once said 'Yesterday's gone' and it's time for a change. Be warned that this part of THIN-THINK requires some courage. Put simply, you may have to decide which you would rather be: *liked* or *thin*.

TO GROUP OR NOT TO GROUP

Many dieters sing the praises of weight loss 'support' groups. These come in various forms, and are clearly popular. Some fatties swear by Weight Watchers or

Overeaters Anonymous. Others simply diet with groups of friends, and claim to thrive on the 'shared' experience.

The downside of 'sharing' is that it means 'going public'. This is anathema to those of us who believe that dieting is essentially a private matter . . . but we may be outnumbered. There's no doubt that 'sharing' is a very 'now' thing to do. Wherever you look in the New Age nineties, someone is 'sharing' his or her experience. (Whether you want them to, or not.) Californians are *crazy* about sharing. Movie stars share intimate details of addictions or neuroses . . . politicians confess marital infidelities. Every third person you meet insists on sharing the pain of childhood abuse, and is keen to swap notes with members of *other* dysfunctional families.

Well, OK. If it works for you, *go for it*. You're bound to find something that's right for you. Heaven knows, there are support groups around which cater for every conceivable human frailty or life crisis, however marginal: Fatties Who Can't Resist Cheesecake. Home-Owners Without Garages. Executives with Missing Filofaxes.

Speaking personally, however, I'd submit that *sharing* is overrated. Staying thin requires a highly-developed sense of self-reliance, determination . . . and personal dignity. If you ask me, SERIOUS DIETERS SHOULD SHARE *NOTHING*. Except dessert. (See Chapter 18, page 247)

FAT-THINK

20

HUNGER: THE ENEMY WITHIN
Fat, Food, Fear . . . and Suffering

At some level, most fatties *fear* hunger. They may not notice – but the first mild signals from an empty-ish tum trigger a sort of primitive 'survival panic'.

No doubt this happens to every member of the human race, since – bungee jumpers apart – we're all programmed for survival. It's just that, in fatties, the reflex is highly developed. The merest hint of gastric contraction catapults body and mind onto 'red alert'. Somewhere at the very heart of FAT-THINK, 'feeling peckish' translates as 'life-threatening'.

I EAT, THEREFORE I AM

Eating, of course, is primarily a response to hunger. But, to complicate matters, fatties can list dozens of *other* reasons for taking in food. They shake down roughly as follows:

I eat because . . .

I'm bored.

I'm anxious and stressed.

I need to be soothed.

I need stimulation.

I'm miserable.

I'm celebrating.

I'm lonely.

People are 'crowding' me.

There's no man/woman in my life.

There are too many men/women in my life.

My mother didn't love me.

My mother smothered me.

It's a way of 'loving' myself.

I want to punish myself.

IN SHORT:

I eat because *I'm alive.*

Wannabe skinnies should try to eat for *one reason only:*

I eat because *I'm hungry.*

It follows that the first step in the achievement of THIN-THINK is to learn to *recognize* hunger. This is not as simple as it sounds, since fatties are inclined to reach for food at the drop of a trauma. With a bit of practice, however, you can retrain your mind to register the difference between 'hungry' and 'comfortable'. So, as your hot little hand gropes yet again for the refrigerator door, or places a Pop Tart in the toaster:

STOP

THINK

QUESTION: AM I HUNGRY?

If the answer is 'no' – **don't eat**! Instead, drink mineral water, or have a coffee or tea (no sugar).

If it's 'yes', or 'getting that way' – choose something appropriate from your diet plan. (No need to wait until you're desperate!) Resist the temptation to go for a 'quick fix' . . . i.e., a chocolate bar or similar. Depending upon the time of day, you may want to 'graze' a bit – or have a main meal. If it's, say, 6 p.m., and you don't expect to eat dinner until eight, use one of your 'spoilers'. Try, for example, a banana, some tomato juice and/or unbuttered wholemeal toast, before *hungry* turns to *starving*, and you lose control.

HUNGER MANAGEMENT

Once you've *recognized* hunger, the next step is to *manage* it. Avoid allowing it to become too intense. And, don't let it frighten you! If you carry low-fat snacks as recommended, you can always deal with it, or 'ward it off'. (A piece of old toast in your pocket is to a hunger pang what garlic on the door is to vampires.) Grazing in this way puts you in charge. You can make sure that hunger remains mild. You can time it . . . or spread it. The point is that *you* control *it* – and not the other way around.

IF IT'S NOT HURTING, IT'S NOT WORKING?

Sixties symbol and singer Marianne Faithfull recently said:

> 'I still feel comfortable when I'm hungry, and bad and wicked when I'm full.'

Few statements more accurately express the female dilemma – though fatties of both sexes experience similar conflicts with food. But, once you've learned to 'manage' hunger – and look it straight in the eye – you may even come to *welcome* it. Those unsettling twinges and spasms are one sign that your diet is working. If you're hungry, your body has used the fuel provided. Calories have been burnt. Now, you're entitled to *more*! That's the good news. The bad news is that, in order to achieve weight loss, you can stoke up only on the usual mind-numbing selection of 'approved' low fat foods.

This is not to suggest that you should get too fond of hunger. The full-scale kind is, of course, a form of pain which is best avoided. Normally, it blots out all other thoughts and feelings until it is relieved. Hungry people feel desperate, and helpless. (The way you do when forced to watch TV shows featuring Loyd Grossman.)

The point is that the prospect of 'suffering' which so frightens fatties is less daunting when *you* are in charge. You can feel confident, because a reliable hand is on the controls. *Yours*. (It also has a reassuring grip on a round of old Melba toast, just in case.) It's up to *you* to decide how much punishment you can take.

Here, too, there's a gender gap. Marianne Faithfull goes on to bemoan women's 'completely neurotic mania with being skeletal'. She is right, of course. Men wish only to have well-toned, healthy bodies, and see no percentage in looking cadaverous. Nor is there clear evidence that they are irresistibly drawn to half-starved women. The fact is that women prefer *themselves* that way. It is fashionable. It speaks volumes about self-control and discipline. And, since – according to a recent report by the Royal College of Physicians – the *higher* up the social scale you go, the *thinner* people get, extreme slimness is also bound up with snobbery. (Princess Di, are you listening?)

More worryingly, designer emaciation seems in some cases a kind of self-inflicted injury. It's easy to use severe calorie restriction as a means of mortifying the flab. To complicate matters, many women hate themselves for being 'fat' – but fear the suffering associated with strict diet . . . then hate themselves *even more* for not having the bottle to endure it.

FEAR OF SUCCESS

Finally, wannabe skinnies face a *different* kind of fear associated with diet. Not fear of *suffering*, but fear of *succeeding*, and becoming slim. Achieving 'the great transformation' can be terrifying. There you are, naked and exposed. Nowhere to hide. No more excuses:

He'd love me if only I were *thin.*

I'd be promoted if only I were *thin.*

I'd enjoy this holiday if only I were *thin*

. . . and so on.

Reach your 'target' weight, and all life's failures come home to roost. You take them on the chin. They accrue directly to you, reflecting your personal inadequacies. You can no longer file them under 'flab'.

FAT-AL ATTRACTION

Furthermore, there's a danger that your new, slim figure will attract interest from the opposite sex. Such attention involves obligation, and *risk* . . . which – subconsciously – fatties may wish to avoid. It is not unusual to 'use' fat as a barrier and protection against life. (It's the best insulation since double glazing.) But, lifelong dieters who repeatedly fail should examine their innermost feelings. It can be enlightening to discover – after years of effort – that a small, subversive part of you is *afraid to be thin*:

Why am I Eating This Chocolate, When I so Much Want to Be Thin?

If I lose weight, men will pursue me.

Some will want dates.

Possibly a passionate, physical relationship.

One may want to marry me.

I'll have decisions to make.

My life will be transformed.

The end of one era . . . the start of another.

Just when I was planning to wash my hair, and watch a video!

Gimme another toffee cream.

21
SURVIVING A 'FAT DAY'

You know the feeling. You wake in the morning feeling
... puffy. Viewed from the side, your tummy looks as if
you snatched the ball from the Harlem Globetrotters –
and swallowed it. Your hair is having an 'off' day, and
manages to look lank and greasy. There's a large pimple

about to blossom in an obtrusive place. You feel ugly and clumsy. Most of all – you feel *fat*.

A '*fat day*' is partly physical – partly psychological. Perhaps you've broken your diet, and overeaten. Having consumed too much, you are now consumed with guilt. Since you know that you *deserve* to be fatter, you punish yourself by *feeling* that way. Or, female fatties may simply be due for a period, and a bit bloated. But, worst of all possibilities is the onset of the dreaded '*plateau*' effect.

This is an (unexplained) phenomenon which can occur at any stage of an otherwise effective diet. It is guaranteed to break the morale of even the most motivated fatty. You are eating as normal, and carefully limiting calories – but the scale unaccountably 'sticks'. Despite your best efforts, there are no further losses. More devastating; weight may begin to show a slight *increase*. 'How much less,' you reflect above the rumbling of your tummy, 'can I possibly eat?' Your sense of injustice is keen. If there is a Supreme Being, He must know that you're hungry. And deserving. So, why aren't you *thin*?

Why?

There is little point in looking to the medical profession for answers. No one seems sure why weight 'plateaus' in this maddening fashion, or even drifts upwards. In females, 'fat days' may be linked to monthly cycle. Or perhaps you're not dieting as strictly as you believe (given the restricted calorie intake necessary for efficient weight loss) even though you're often hungry. It may be that fatties run foul of some little-known metabolic perversity; a kind of sporadic *starve and grow fat* syndrome.

Whatever the explanation, 'fat days' are the pits . . . the nadir of human existence. They are not only deeply disappointing, but – worse – defeating. You want to give up, but life seems to demand yet more sacrifice. Spiritually speaking, you've 'hit the wall'. You've nothing left to give . . . and nothing left to *eat*.

What to do? Your first instinct is to OD on junk food. You reach automatically for the nearest packet of Wotsits, hoping for inspiration (Wotsit All About?). But, the most likely answer is that you're a victim of *dieter's drift* (the tendency to increase calories and relax controls as diets begin to produce results). If so, here are a few tips:

Survival Strategies

1. DRESS FOR SUCCESS

On a 'fat day', the temptation is to climb miserably into your oldest, darkest and loosest clothes. Don't. This will serve only to make you feel frumpier. Instead, choose a reliable outfit which always looks flattering. Something with an 'easy' fit . . . not loose and sloppy – but not too demanding, either. (This is not the day for your skin-tight leather jeans and matching biker jacket.)

The better you look, the more 'in charge' you will feel, and the better equipped to survive a 'fat day'. Strong motivation comes when there's something *important* to protect. Hard to muster much resolve when a glance in the mirror reveals a spotty unwashed chub in a shapeless shell-suit.

2. 'ZAP' SPARE CALORIES

'I'm eating next to nothing,' you protest. 'Impossible to eat less!' When you're dieting strenuously, and your idea of a 'blow-out' is a glass of skimmed milk and a Wheat-Thin, it's hard to see what more to cut. The only encouraging fact is that, sometimes when a strict diet is 'stalled', a *small* further reduction in calories seems to make a *big* difference (like applying jump-leads to an engine). So, it's worth having another sift through your menu for 'empty' or spare calories. Here's a quick check-list:

   a. Any remaining sugar in coffee or tea.

   b. Any wine (or other alcohol).

   c. Any butter, margarine or butter substitute
      (however polyunsaturated).

   d. Any dressing on salads (even if you're using a
      'low-fat' dieter's dressing or the occasional
      tablespoon of salad oil). Limit yourself – at least
      temporarily – to plain lemon juice or vinegar.

   e. Any 'diet' colas or soft drinks (even if they
      claim to contain 'no calories').

3. INCREASE FRUIT AND VEG

Many dieters stray away from these at the first opportunity. Given the (low-fat) choice between a raw vegetable salad and a plate of pasta, they'll choose the pasta every time. If your diet is 'stalled', think of the food you are *least* likely to choose when hungry. A fresh orange? A celery stick? Dead give-away. Make a renewed effort to include these in your diet. The elimination of fruit 'n' veg (friendliest of diet fodder) may effectively add unwanted calories to your daily menu.

4. REVIEW PORTION SIZE

Have these crept gradually up since you began dieting? Do you feel comfortably able to get away with *smaller* servings (bearing in mind the option of 'grazing' during the day if you find you're hungry)? Take another look at that nightly chicken breast, portion of lean beef or fillet of poached fish. Does it still resemble the 3 to 4 ounce serving featured on page 70? Or does it look more like a snack for Demis Roussos? Try cutting it in half, and see how you feel.

5. EAT YOUR LAST MEAL OF THE DAY EARLIER

Remember that six hours should ideally elapse between your final meal, and bedtime. Eating fashionably late because of business or social commitments can seriously damage your diet . . . even if you stick virtuously to a low-fat menu. If you're convinced that the composition of your evening meal is correct, *continue to do exactly what you're doing* – but do it one to two hours *earlier*.

If this isn't practical – or fails to produce the results you want – try swapping dinner and lunch, and have your largest meal at midday. There's some truth to the old adage that you should eat like a king at breakfast, a prince at lunchtime, and a pauper at dinner . . . (except that wannabe skinnies should eat as if penniless *three* times a day).

6. TAKE A HARD LOOK AT YOUR WEEKEND 'TREAT'

When you 'break' your diet regularly as recommended (Chapter 18, Tip 18), it's supposed to provide a small reward for getting through a difficult week. Small is not a blow-out. Small means approximately 300 calories – or fewer, if you can manage. If you've been having a chocolate bar, try cutting it in half. If you're choosing an ice cream cone – share with a friend. As a last resort, try going *without* your treat for one weekend only . . . and see if it makes a difference.

7. EXERCISE INGENUITY

First, turn off the TV. Then, face facts. Have you been *exercising* less than usual . . . or 'sitting still' more? Perhaps there are reasons. (The weather's been rotten,' you've been ill . . . or catching up on sedentary tasks, like paying bills.) Anyway, if you've let your usual physical routine slip, try shaking your 'stalled' metabolism from its torpor. Walk to the shops, and leave the car behind. Reorganize a closet. If you work several floors up in an office block, climb the stairs each morning instead of using the lift. You get the picture.

Shopping is, of course, good exercise, too. Wander from store to store, browse to your heart's content ('comparison' shopping saves money – and burns calories!) You can look at furniture, household items, or clothing for your family. Just one word of caution: *never* (on a 'fat day') be tempted to shop for clothes for *yourself*. Try nothing on. (To do so in a 'fat' frame of mind achieves little, and may even be harmful to your psyche.) Above all, avoid the most *reckless* and *dangerous* thing any dieter can do on a 'fat day'. Under no circumstances should you:

Try on Bathing Suits

Nothing is guaranteed to make you feel worse about yourself. Shiny, heavy-duty stretch fabrics emphasize flaws – and somehow 'rearrange' every spare ounce of cellulite. Midriff bulge is pushed down around your waist. Fat backs and ample chests take up new positions under your arms. *Women's* bathing suits are, as ever, the worst offenders. The most unbecoming garments ever created, today's fashions are cut extra-high on the hips, so as to reveal every inch of unsightly flab between waist and thigh – plus a fair bit of stubble. For despairing fatties, 'ordeal by swimwear' invites disaster. You can't survive a 'fat day' by becoming suicidal.

8. 'DIETER'S DRIFT'

Finally, on a 'fat day' it's worth considering one other possibility. You may be experiencing 'dieter's drift'. Don't forget that most fatties must maintain a 'deficit' of at least 500 calories a day in order to lose approximately one pound a week (see p. 266). This allows very little 'margin for error'. If you're not careful, a few 'extras' here and there can soon mount up. For example: a flavoured 'low-fat' yogurt – even a small one – can easily be worth 80 calories. Add a medium-sized glass of orange juice, and the total pushes 200. Throw caution to the winds with one digestive biscuit (*without* chocolate coating) and you've added another 60 calories.

The message is that, at every stage of a weight-loss diet, intake must be tightly controlled. Things will 'ease' a bit when you move to a maintenance diet ... but only a bit. A glance at these figures is revealing. It shows that many people 'give up' on diets because *they're not really*

dieting. (They may be *suffering* ... but that's not the same thing.) That's why it's so important to cut calories in a way which produces results. Only a glutton for punishment would prolong the misery.

22

SURGERY – THE FINAL SOLUTION

If You Can't Starve It Off – Can You Cut It Off?

It's a fact that diets are uncomfortable, dull, joyless, unfair, frustrating, and – above all – *long*. So, it's not surprising that some seek a 'quick fix'. Even if it's risky. Even if it's imperfect. Even if it's expensive. Even if it hurts. Many fatties prefer almost *anything* to the long-term, low-level pain of calorie restriction.

Liposuction is, of course, the cosmetic procedure (normally carried out by plastic surgeons) which literally 'sucks' excess fat from beneath the skin. It is intended, we're told, for stubborn 'pockets of cellulite' which ordinary dieting won't shift.

A bit of scepticism is called for. The world is full of disheartened and weary dieters who may see surgery as a shortcut – or, worse still, as an *alternative* – to changing eating habits. The search for a 'magic bullet' – in the form of liposuction, meal replacements, or dependence upon artificial sweeteners – is bound to end in disappointment. It is fundamental FAT-THINK.

This is not to say that liposuction is *never* appropriate. But the procedure should not be misused, or undertaken lightly. *Diet* must remain the first (and, in most cases, *only*) line of treatment. Not a popular idea with those impatient for 'instant' results.

UNPALATABLE TRUTH

And, what's all this about 'pockets of cellulite'? (Otherwise known as deposits of fat.) To say that they're 'stubborn' implies that they don't respond to strict and sustained diet.

Yes. Well. Ever seen TV pictures of East African famine victims? Ever been offended by unsightly 'pockets of cellulite'? Of course not. While it's true that excess body fat tends, in many of us, to 'clump' in specific areas ('why does everything I eat go straight to my hips?') it is seldom truly impervious to conscientious calorie-cutting.

Make no mistake: surgery traumatizes the body, and cannot resolve a fatty's *basic* problem. It is certainly no substitute for conventional diet. So, before allowing anyone to approach you with sharp instruments, take stock of the following:

1. Have you genuinely changed your eating habits, and maintained new ones for extended periods? (Try cutting out dessert before you do the same to flab.)

2. Surgery won't make you THIN. It may deflate your problem thighs or knees but no one has yet found a way to liposuction *whole bodies*.

23
THIN AT LAST!
The Very Best Things About Being Thin

There are umpteen good reasons for losing weight –
many of which have been covered here. Fatties will
rehearse them again and again in the course of a long
diet, to boost flagging will-power. It's important, too, to
have a list of compelling *incentives* on which you can
draw. *Clothing* often works well; buying new clothes,
needing smaller ones, or looking good in the ones you've
got. A new *love interest* is probably the next best thing.
(If married, re-cycle the *old* one.)

For fatties who need additional inspiration, here is a
final 'THIN AT LAST' check-list; .

If You're a Woman, The REAL Rewards of Being Slim Are:

1. Hearing people say that you've got a great
   body.

2. Needing a smaller size.

3. Knowing that you can wear clingy clothes
   without remembering to pull your tummy in.

4. Feeling perfectly at ease in communal fitting rooms.

5. Sitting on his lap without fear of *crushing* him.

6. Slipping easily out of the car on the kerbside, even when an obstruction means that the door only opens half way.

7. Noticing that your tights no longer 'ball up' on the inside thighs.

8. Accepting boxes of chocolates without feeling like Miss Piggy.

9. Finding that new friends are 'amazed' to learn that you *ever* had a weight problem.

10. Feeling confident that the hotel's complimentary towelling bathrobe is going to fit. So is the 'smock' provided by your hairdresser.

11. Discovering that your expensive body lotion seems to go further.

12. Realizing that he could *lift* you, if he felt like it, without risking a hernia.

If You're a Man, the REAL Rewards of Being Slim Are:

1. Jeans, trousers and jockey shorts which no longer lodge *under* the 'overhang' of your stomach or pull down to reveal a bare lower back.

2. Being able to tie your shoelaces from a standing position.

3. Discovering that your arches are no longer flat.

4. Changing clothes at the sports centre or swimming pool without ducking into a separate cubicle.

4. Daring to mow the lawn minus your shirt.

5. Hoping that the blonde next door is looking.

6. Managing to fit more water in the bathtub.

7. Driving your car without being forced to sit in the *back seat*. (Realizing, at last, *why* the seat is adjustable.)

8. Noticing that the writing on your T-shirt no longer *distorts* over the stomach.

9. Sunbathing on the beach without searching for a secluded spot.

10. Noting with pride that the seat of your bicycle doesn't disappear when you sit on it.

11. Best of all – she can get *both* arms around you. And your side of the bed doesn't sink.

And . . . *for* ALL *Former Fatties, Here Are the Very* BEST *Things About Being Slim:*

1. People stop advising you to 'lose weight' and start asking how you *did* it.

2. Needing to re-heel your shoes less often.

3. Standing tall and unashamed in the queue at the 'Mr Whippy' van.

4. Running up four flights with ease.

5. Feeling healthy, energetic . . . and young!

6. Looking attractive and sexy with *no* clothes on.

7. Hearing the doctor say you're in great shape.

8. Knowing that you can afford to eat the *whole* cone if you like . . . but that you'll only take two bites.

AND – THE GREATEST PLEASURE OF ALL:

9. Realising that you're finally *thin enough* . . . and free to think about other things!

Because the *real* reward of slimness is that you can stop worrying about trying to GET thin – and start worrying about trying to STAY that way.

NOTE

This book is intended to promote a disciplined and determined attitude to controlled dieting. Any reader who is not in good mental or physical health or who is in any doubt about any aspect of dieting should consult a doctor before attempting to lose weight.

READ MORE IN PENGUIN

In every corner of the world, on every subject under the sun, Penguin represents quality and variety – the very best in publishing today.

For complete information about books available from Penguin – including Puffins, Penguin Classics and Arkana – and how to order them, write to us at the appropriate address below. Please note that for copyright reasons the selection of books varies from country to country.

In the United Kingdom: Please write to *Dept. JC, Penguin Books Ltd, FREEPOST, West Drayton, Middlesex UB7 0BR*

If you have any difficulty in obtaining a title, please send your order with the correct money, plus ten per cent for postage and packaging, to *PO Box No. 11, West Drayton, Middlesex UB7 0BR*

In the United States: Please write to *Penguin USA Inc., 375 Hudson Street, New York, NY 10014*

In Canada: Please write to *Penguin Books Canada Ltd, 10 Alcorn Avenue, Suite 300, Toronto, Ontario M4V 3B2*

In Australia: Please write to *Penguin Books Australia Ltd, 487 Maroondah Highway, Ringwood, Victoria 3134*

In New Zealand: Please write to *Penguin Books (NZ) Ltd, 182–190 Wairau Road, Private Bag, Takapuna, Auckland 9*

In India: Please write to *Penguin Books India Pvt Ltd, 706 Eros Apartments, 56 Nehru Place, New Delhi 110 019*

In the Netherlands: Please write to *Penguin Books Netherlands B.V., Keizersgracht 231 NL–1016 DV Amsterdam*

In Germany: Please write to *Penguin Books Deutschland GmbH, Friedrichstrasse 10–12, W–6000 Frankfurt/Main 1*

In Spain: Please write to *Penguin Books S. A., C. San Bernardo 117–6° E–28015 Madrid*

In Italy: Please write to *Penguin Italia s.r.l., Via Felice Casati 20, I–20124 Milano*

In France: Please write to *Penguin France S. A., 17 rue Lejeune, F–31000 Toulouse*

In Japan: Please write to *Penguin Books Japan, Ishikiribashi Building, 2–5–4, Suido, Tokyo 112*

In Greece: Please write to *Penguin Hellas Ltd, Dimocritou 3, GR–106 71 Athens*

In South Africa: Please write to *Longman Penguin Southern Africa (Pty) Ltd, Private Bag X08, Bertsham 2013*